GW00361389

"DEAR MERV . . . DEAR BILL"

"Dear Merv . . . Dear Bill"

Mervyn Haisman

and

L. E. Snellgrove

Foreword by
Gavin Young

First Impression — 1992

ISBN 0 86383 890 1

© Mervyn Haisman and L. E. Snellgrove

All rights reserved. No part of this book may be reproduced, stored in a retrieval system, or transmitted in any form or by any means, electronic, electrostatic, magnetic tape, mechanical, photocopying, recording or otherwise, without permission in writing from the publishers, Gomer Press, Llandysul, Dyfed, Wales.

Printed in Wales by
J. D. Lewis and Sons Ltd., Gomer Press, Llandysul, Dyfed, Wales

'This Mischievous Book'
is dedicated to
VICTORIA ARMSTRONG

FOREWORD

Many years ago—and also many years after the goings-on recounted in this book—I found myself in a remote town on the edge of the Arabian desert, the Empty Quarter. It was Christmas Day, and in a heavy mood of nostalgia for Britain I turned on my Zenith radio and tuned in to the BBC's Overseas Service. Almost at once a warm, strong unaccented voice began reading a wonderful piece of prose about Christmas in the countryside of South Wales.

Sitting in the sand, surrounded by a group of disinterested Beduins, I wondered how the reader came to have had the same recollections of carol-singing down snow-filled Welsh lanes that I had.

The voice took me back to wartime evenings at Christmas-time spent wandering between dark country hedgerows near Lower Machen in Gwent, accompanied by four or five twelve-year-old ragamuffins from Eltham (Merv prominent among them), and I saw us in the dark hurrying nervously past the blasted oak tree from which a sinister figure had once leaped out on Myfanwy Spooner as she cycled home in the black-out.

The radio talk ended and an announcer said the reader had been Dylan Thomas. Of course. But that reading had started something in my mind. The Queen came on next for her Christmas broadcast, but I hardly heard a word of what she said. I was back in the garden of my uncle's house, confronting a menacing bunch of dead-end kids in knee-length shorts and ankle socks, rolling up their sleeves (at least figuratively) preparatory to setting about this toffy-nosed prep-schoolboy who seemed to intend spending *his* holidays in *their* garden. The one boy who wore long trousers and who looked more threatening than all the rest, was Mervyn Haisman.

It seems we overcame our mutual and instinctive hostility almost at once. For in next to no time I was being carpeted by my outraged uncle who accused me of being the gang-leader responsible for stealing the lead and breaking every last piece of glass in the greenhouse roof. Why, he roared, I was behaving like a—well, like a damned *evacuee*! If I didn't pull myself together, he would have to ask my mother to send me away.

Of course I remember Mervyn very well—better, I suppose, than any of the other evacuees except a pale and gentle boy called Charles Burton who became my particular friend, and who was, as Mervyn explains in this book, soon killed by a German land mine. I suppose that was the first time that real tragedy had intruded into my life, and I remember now how deeply I was shocked at Charles' death. It was a dangerous time and now I come to think of it, even in the idyllic Welsh countryside we could hear the nightly rumble of the anti-aircraft guns from Newport and Cardiff, and listen to the terrifying whistle and crash of shrapnel falling among snow-covered fields and the woods around us. If we were a rowdy lot, breaking greenhouses and threatening to rape Jenny, the maid (she knew we were only joking), our behaviour was only a pale copy of the far greater violence around us—the violence of the adult world at war.

How lucky that that trousered twelve-year-old hooligan called Mervyn Haisman grew up to be a writer. What a joy to re-visit through his eyes, and those of his good friend Bill Snellgrove, those long-ago days of youth and innocence. Well, comparative innocence.

Gavin Young

Front garden, Kenward Rd., 1939

Front garden, Kenward Rd., 1991

Herbert Hospital,
Woolwich, S.E.18.
1st September 1939

Dear Merv,

It looks as though there's going to be a war so I'm sending this to Kenward Road. When you are evacuated your Dad can send it on once you write and tell him where you are. That is, if you ever do write! You've only written TWO letters since I was carted off to this prison. And what about your promise to cycle up here and see me?

Sorry to grumble but I'm really fed up. The whole world's on the brink of war and here am I stuck in bed with rotten glandular fever. The sun's blazing through the windows and the rotten nurses won't let me get up. There's just no fun for me anymore. And the thought of you and the others going off on adventures without me is sickening.

Stuck here in bed, with nothing to do, I worked out that I still have 1,253 lines to write for different teachers. My favourite is, 'I must not pour milk over Gladys Dickenson's head.' But with old Grindle out of the way he won't be able to cane me, so I shan't write a line. Still, that's

The Assembly Hall at Eltham Central School where we were told about the evacuation

not important. What really matters is to keep me informed because I'm going to be left behind. I've worked it all out. I'm going to stop writing my life of Napoleon and make notes for a HISTORY OF THE WAR. This is where YOU come in.

You MUST write and tell me what happens. There could be a lightning attack by sea or land before I'm even up and about.I know you're interested in Joan Longley, but please Merv, this is history! You needn't put in anything about yourself, only things about the war. Just give me facts. As Grindle's always telling you, 'show some sense of responsibility'. I know you don't like history, but the one thing you are good at is writing, so write! As soon as you get to wherever you're going, please send me your address.

Cheerio,
Bill

13, Kenward Road,
Eltham, London, S.E.9.
1st September 1939

Dear Bill,

I know I promised to come and see you in hospital, but so much has been happening I just haven't had the time. Still, I expect you're having plenty of visitors and I didn't want to catch what you've got anyway because Mum says it takes a long time to get over. From the sound of it, you could be stuck there for quite a long while. So, even though you're lying there tucked up in bed and enjoying life, I still thought you might like to know what's happening in the world outside.

Well, first of all there's going to be a WAR. I expect your Mum and Dad have been keeping it from you so you don't worry, but everyone in our street says so and my brother Eric, who as you know works in Woolwich Arsenal, said last night that it was definite! And he should certainly know because he's making all the bombs and bullets and shells and things. But here's the really important news, Bill.

Tomorrow we're going to be evacuated!!! Everyone's terribly excited and as you'll still be stuck in hospital and won't be coming, I thought the least I could do was write and tell you what's going on, so that you can be on guard against bombs and things.

Here's what happened. At school today we did absolutely nothing, except write out our name and Eltham Central School on half a dozen labels—which took up all of ten minutes. No lessons at all, which as it being a Friday we were due to have a whole hour of French, really pleased me. All the teachers kept on coming and going and getting together in groups and running round in circles like a lot of lost sheep. No one did a stroke of work! It was wonderful. Then, straight after dinner break, the whole school was called into Assembly. All the teachers on the platform were very solemn and Grindle in the middle trying to look calm and collected.

First of all we sang God Save The King—which was the second time that day. Then he told us, that as there was a vague possibility that there might be a war, and just as a precaution, we were to be evacuated. He couldn't tell us where we were going and probably in a few weeks it would all be over and we'd be back home again. Then he said that we all had to be at Well Hall station at nine tomorrow and we could only take one suitcase. As soon as he stopped speaking Mrs Boon suddenly started to sing Rule Britannia, which really shook old Grindle as he wasn't expecting it, and as she was trying to sing and cry at the same time it sounded pretty awful. Lastly, as a practice, he made us put on our gasmasks to numbers. When he called out three, the whole school breathed out making the noise of a mighty FART, which sounded wonderful and gave Mrs Boon hiccups.

So, that's it, Bill. I can't tell you where we're going because I don't know. Someone reckoned on Scotland but my guess is Cornwall. Anyway, I promise to write once I get there. I bet you wish you were going.

Your friend,
Merv

57, St. Mary's Road,
Deal, Kent.
6th September 1939

Dear Bill,

As you can see, we've been evacuated to Deal. Last Saturday morning we left Well Hall station dead on ten. I made a point of checking the time on the new Ingersol watch Dad gave me because you seemed to be in such a state about this war even before it started. Anyway, ten o'clock is a fact. And here's another one. We didn't get to Deal until seven ! I wanted to get billeted with Freddie Jackson but got stuck with Walter Pugh from 4A. I don't think you know him. He's fat and wears glasses and thinks he can tell me what to do just because he's in a higher class. He's got a dressing gown, which is not really surprising as he lives in Avery Hill, and his father works for Martins Bank.

We ended up staying with two women. They're called Pym. One of them has a dress shop and the other does nothing. Walter says they're sisters but I think they're cousins. There's a sea captain's hat on the hallstand. They keep it there so that people will believe there's a man in the house. If you could see them Bill, you'd wonder why they bother.

The house is right on the front and we have a room at the top. There's only electricity downstairs, so we have to take a candle to bed. The first night we kept hearing boards creaking, and what with the one flickering candle it was all a bit spooky. I told Walter the house was probably haunted and it was the ghost coming to get him. I tried to make him scared but he just laughed, so in the end I went to sleep. But in the morning I found out that he'd stayed awake all night and the Pyms told him off for wasting a whole candle. I hope the house isn't haunted.

The Pyms don't take sugar. They said it was bad for us and going without would make Walter lose weight. So, just because he's fat, I can't have sugar. If you haven't tasted cocoa without sugar, don't try!!

Last Sunday, after Chamberlain told us we were at war, they took us for a walk and when we got to Walmer Castle the siren went. We took

12

Central schoolgirls waiting for the evacuation train

shelter in the dungeons and one of the Pyms (the one who doesn't work), started to cry. We were there for a whole half hour and nothing happened, except for Miss Pym crying all the time. Then the All Clear sounded and we went back to the house. But they kept us in all afternoon just in case something did happen—which it didn't.

Walter found a telescope and took it up to our bedroom to watch out for bombers. This was a complete waste of time because there weren't any. I don't suppose he knows what a German bomber looks like anyway.

We haven't started school yet and yesterday, Miss Pym (the dress shop one), took us hop picking. It was very hot and one of the men gave me some cider. It's powerful stuff! Afterwards I had to sit down for a bit. My hands are still yellow from the hops but I earned 1/6!!! How's your glandular fever and when will you get out?

Your friend,

Merv

P.S. Let me know if anyone reads your letters.

7, Nesbit Road,
Eltham, S.E.9.
12th September 1939

Dear Merv,

Thank you for your letter. It gave me your address. As you can see, I'm back at home but still in bed. They chucked me out of the hospital. Something about needing the beds for wounded soldiers. I can't see how many British soldiers can be wounded as our army hasn't gone anywhere yet.

You're a lucky old bean to be by the sea. I've only been to the seaside once. That was a couple of years ago with Teddy Baldock's mum and dad. We went to Bognor and Teddie's dad took a picture of me in the sea, just the head showing. What on earth did you do for nine hours in a train? What does Deal look like and has it got a pier? What do the Pyms look like? I mean, are they fat or thin, long or short or similar, like Tweedledum and Tweedledee? Things like this worry you when you're laid up in bed and your best friend is having adventures and there is an exciting war on somewhere.

What about the 'Athenia' going down? They should try 'Q' Ships like they did in the Great War. Looked like an innocent ship but had guns hidden in the sides. Then when the U Boat came to the surface, the sides dropped down and the gunners let them have it.

The papers say there are lots of Italian ships off Deal and Dover. They are being held in case the Italians declare war. I suppose that what with the Pym women, hop picking and frightening fat Walter, you haven't even noticed them. Do please keep your eyes open and let me know any news. I'm really fed up here, though dad says it's not worth getting up because there's nothing to do. No cinemas, no lights, no kids, nothing. You'd think the Pied Piper had been through Eltham,I heard him tell my mum. He hoped I hadn't heard but I had and it made me feel even more fed up. I haven't started on my history of this war yet and unless you give me some more details I'll never get started. So, as Mrs Boon often tells us, 'overcome your natural sloth'—and WRITE!

Cheerio,
Bill

14

P.S. Just remembered your P.S. As I've only had letters from uncles and aunts before I don't know if they will be read, but mum and dad NEVER read my diary so I think it's all right.

57, St. Mary's Road,
Deal, Kent.
22nd September 1939

Dear Bill,

Bad news!! We start school on Monday. Ronnie Johnson told me we should have started school at least a week ago but Mr Morgan lost the lists of where we were all staying. Since then, the teachers have been running around town, knocking on doors trying to track us all down. So, yesterday when I saw old Morgan coming along the road, I naturally did what you would have done and ducked down behind the hedge. Only just then Walter spotted him from the front room, rushed out of the house and called out to him. He really is a fool. When Morgan saw me crouching down I told him I was studying the behaviour of a stag beetle. I thought that would please him as he's always going on about insects and things in his lessons. Luckily for me, he didn't ask to see it.

Your letters are full of moans and questions. I suppose that if I don't tell you everything about the evacuation you'll only keep on at me. And as Morgan said we'd have to write an essay about it anyway, here goes.

Your letter from the hospital, arrived on the Saturday, just before we left. Mum was to have come to the station but she started to cry. Dad told her not to be so bloody stupid but that only made her cry more. I've never seen her cry before. Then Dad took me into the front room and gave me the new Ingersol pocket watch I told you about. Five shillings he said it cost. Plus a bag of plums he'd picked from next door's garden—not Mrs Greenset's—the other side—they're the ones we don't talk to!

15

Mervyn's father, John Josiah Haisman, dressed for the beach

I think Dad was right about women, because when we got to the station most of the mothers were crying—so was your Cynthia Agnew. Perhaps she was missing you. (Big laugh). I tried to get in a carriage with Joan Longley but rotten Mrs Boon stopped me. Freddie Jackson and I were put in a compartment in charge of six first form boys, and within five minutes of leaving the station, they were all crying their eyes out. I think this was partly because Freddie told them how the Germans always machine gunned trains, especially those carrying children, and that we were all travelling towards certain death. Anyway, I soon got fed up with all their howling and made them crawl under the seats because it was safer. It was a good half hour before they came out again, by which time Freddie and I had drunk all their milk.

A lot of the plums were rotten, so every time we went through a station we threw them at people. All of Freddie's missed and I only hit one old man in the back of the neck. The trick is, to throw behind the target. The pity was, we only discovered this with my last plum, so it's really only a theory. When you're up and about you might care to experiment from the top deck of a tram. (I think you'll find that the 46 tram goes faster than the 72). Anyway, let me know the results.

I don't think anyone knew where we were going—least of all the train driver. We kept on stopping. Few more miles; then we'd stop again. And we stopped in one tunnel for at least half an hour. (That's when I wished I'd managed to get in with Joan Longley). We even went backwards three times! Freddie said we were changing lines to fool the Germans. I think we just got lost. After one long wait in the middle of nowhere, women suddenly appeared with biscuits, cakes and cups of tea. Of course, we had to be at the back of the train and just as they got to us, it started moving again. By the time we got to Margate it was late afternoon. We thought we were going to stay there, but oh no. We sat in that train for an hour, then we all had to get out and get into charabancs. Except that there were only two of them and we had to wait for more to arrive.

I didn't see Grindle. Being a headmaster, perhaps he had a train all to himself. By this time the teachers were all shouting at one another—except Mrs Boon who kept clapping her hands and calling out,'Now then, now then everybody', only no one listened. Finally, we drove for miles and miles until we got to Deal station. I couldn't understand why we didn't just stay on the train. Freddie reckoned it was because they'd only bought tickets to Margate. Anyway, there were a whole crowd of grown-ups waiting for us. They call them foster-parents. Some wanted boys, some wanted girls. When they'd taken their pick there were still fifty of us left and so we wandered around town with the teachers knocking on doors like brush salesmen. Freddie got taken in early—soon after he'd suddenly decided to develop a limp— crafty bugger. By now it was gone nine o' clock and what with this black-out and no lights anywhere, we could hardly see where we were—not that anyone cared by then. They talked about sleeping some of us in the police station which would have been fun, but then the Pyms took us in. Yes, Deal has got a pier.

Walter says he's going for a swim and wants me to go with him, so I'll carry on tomorrow.

23rd September

Bill, I can swim!!! I learnt yesterday afternoon. It's easy. I watched Walter swimming. He's so fat, he just floats. After he'd called me a cissy and I'd thrown stones at him, Joan Longley and Cynthia Agnew appeared, so I could hardly stay out of the water, could I? Walter saw them and started to show off doing the side-stroke, so I copied him— and it worked. There I was, swimming!! Unfortunately, by then Joan had gone. Just my luck. At the moment I can only swim one way, facing the beach. I've tried it the other way but the waves go up my nose. It just means I have to keep on getting out, walking back and starting again, which is a bit of a nuisance—particularly as it's a pebble beach.

The news is not as bad as I thought. Eltham Central is sharing a school, so we will only be going in the mornings. We've heard quite a few explosions out at sea—mines I expect—but haven't actually seen anything. There's been no shipwrecks, no bodies in drifting lifeboats and no air raids. Have you had any in London?

This is probably the longest letter I've ever written, so don't keep complaining! I only write a page to Mum and Dad each week to thank them for my 1/6 postal order. Walter Pugh gets 2/6. How much do you get?

Your friend,
Merv

18

Dear Merv,

I've looked very carefully but there are no drifting lifeboats in Eltham High Street. All the same, thanks for the details which will go into my History of the War. I'll not report your swimming exploits as somehow I don't think this will affect the course of the war.

There's no news from this end except that I'm now up and about and still very bored. Before the war, dad used to say that the moment it started, or within twenty-four hours—whichever was the sooner—you would walk in a shop, ask for something quite ordinary and be told, 'Don't you know there's a war on?' Well, as there's nothing happening up here, I decided to carry on with my life of Napoleon, so I went to Woolworths to buy another sixpenny notebook. It's no use me getting the cheap ones—I write too much. The stationery counter

Bill's father in Oxford, 1949

19

looked almost empty and the assistant said with a scowl, 'We're waiting for another delivery. After all, there is a war on'. So dad was not far out in his prediction.

My own theory is, that as soon as war was declared, orders were given at HQ to empty every Woolworths in the country, just in case anybody wanted to buy anything. A sort of war effort which would be a bit different. The sweet counter is completely empty. Not a bar of chocolate in sight. Dad says they've all gone to the soldiers who aren't wounded. What a Christmas it's going to be!

To answer your questions about air raids—there haven't been any. I can't understand where all the bombers we were told about have got to. Do you remember the newsreels showing the Spanish Civil War bombing? I was expecting real excitement, ruins and all that by now. All we've got is a black-out which will make winter worse. There was an accident between a cyclist and a car last night, right outside our house. I wasn't surprised because it was pitch black! Every day people keep on walking into pillar boxes and tripping over things. Dad says we could lose the war by killing everyone in the black-out. The Germans won't need to do a thing.

Two days ago a Warden, old Rogers, knocked on the door and told dad he was showing a light. We had a tiny chink in the curtaining and you could only just see it if you bent down in the garden. Dad asked him if he thought the German Air Force was coming by underground. There was a bit of an argument and dad ended up calling him a little Hitler, which really upset old Rogers. Otherwise there has been no FUN at all. I do miss everyone—even the teachers—even you.

Please write soon.

Cheerio,
Bill

57, St. Mary's Road,
Deal, Kent.
28th October 1939

Dear Bill,

Thank you for your letter. Our Woolworths hasn't got any chocolate either.

It's Saturday and I'm stuck indoors because my postal order hasn't arrived. It always comes on a Friday. I have a nagging worry that something terrible has happened at Kenward Road. There was no mention of Kenward Road or Eltham on the radio, only I'm sure they don't tell us everything in case spies are listening. Please go round there and let me know. But if my parents are alive and well, tell them that I can't exist on 1/6 a week. Or better still, let them know that Walter Pugh gets 2/6. Just drop it into the conversation casually.

Last Sunday, my brother Eric came down on his new Black Panther. As you know, he used to have a Red Panther, but this one's much more powerful. My sister Vevlie came with him on the pillion. She'd burnt her leg on the exhaust and was blue with cold, so she didn't talk much to begin with, just shivered. It was all right for Eric because he had on his waders, helmet and rubber greatcoat. Dad always says he looks like a bloody deep sea diver and I think he's right. Mum and Dad sent down some winter clothes and a Waterman's fountain pen with a gold nib! Eric bought me a handline and wanted to go fishing on the pier, but you can't get out to the end of it because they've taken out some planks to stop the Germans landing. I suppose they think they're coming in paddle-steamers! So we just walked around, only Vevlie couldn't stop shivering. In the end she got her own way and we went into a cafe and had tea.

Vevlie's working up at Cannon Street now and Eric's still at Woolwich Arsenal. He's in the Danger Buildings making shells and bombs and things. They're working twenty-four hours a day, but you'd better not spread this around. I thought you'd like to know for historical reasons. They left early because Eric doesn't like driving with this new slotted mask over the headlight, says you can't see a thing. I suppose they got home all right, but as I haven't heard they

21

Eric, looking like a 'bloody deep-sea diver'   Mervyn's sister, Vevlie

could be dead for all I know. Perhaps that's why Mum hasn't written, not wanting to worry me. She's very thoughtful about things like that.

I quite like the Pyms now. We call them Auntie Kitty and Auntie Freddie—sounds odd but it's short for Winifred. Kitty's a bit scatty and never stops twittering. She's either laughing or crying, but she's a smashing cook. Freddie's the one I really like. She's got a deep voice and sounds a bit like a man. And she smokes like a chimney— Capstain Full Strength!!! She offered me one while I was helping her with the gardening, only I couldn't finish it. They are really strong! I told her I normally smoked Weights and the next day when Kitty wasn't looking, she slipped me a packet of five! This week, on her half-day, we went fishing with the line that Eric gave me and we caught a cod. A fisherman told us it was really a codling, but all the same it was a big fish. We had it for supper that night and there was still some left over for fishcakes.

Oh yes, here's something that will interest you, Bill. While we were fishing, a plane flew over with a big circle of wire going all the way around it. It kept on flying backwards and forwards really low over the sea—only about twenty feet up. Suddenly, a mine went up in the water just behind it. Then another one went off. We could see it all quite clearly as it wasn't very far out. The spray must have gone up nearly a hundred feet and the explosions were absolutely terrific. You should have been here, it was smashing! One of the hotels on the front had two windows broken. Auntie Freddie says this was caused by the blast. She reckoned that the mines were the magnetic type and that the wire around the plane was probably copper, so that it made an electrical circuit and it was this that triggered off the mines. Funny that a woman should know all about things like that. Especially when you think of my Aunt Lizzy. She won't have electricity in her house because she believes it leaks. Anyway, I thought you'd like to know all about this for historical reasons.

How's the War going in Eltham? There's nothing much happening down here and some of the boys have gone back home. Saw Deanna Durbin in 'That Certain Age'. She sings quite well but it was a sloppy story and Walter went to sleep. Our class is going to do The Barretts of Wimpole Street—and don't laugh—I'm going to play Robert Browning. I'd far rather play the old man as it's a bigger part and he has to do a lot of shouting.

Would you believe it? Auntie Kitty has just told me that my letter did come yesterday and she's been carrying it around in her apron pocket ever since. She really is a dizzy woman. Will finish now as I want to get to the Post Office to cash my P.O.

Your friend,
Merv

23

7, Nesbit Road,
Eltham, S.E.9.
16th November 1939

Dear Merv,

Two windows broken, eh? Things are obviously hotting up at your end. Aeroplanes as well? But thanks for the news anyway. Your Auntie Freddie seems to know a lot about mines and things. Are you sure she's a woman? After all she is called Freddie. She might even be a spy!

Good news at last! They've opened a school for us. I suppose it wasn't easy. At least three, including Deansfield Road, are either Fire depots or used by Civil Defence. Anyway, I met Roberts in the High Street about a week ago. His parents brought him back from Deal because there was no bombing in London. Told me what a fine time you were having. He said they were opening up some classrooms at Eltham Hill Girls School; you know, the one next to the Odeon. They were to be for Central School people from Eltham, Woolwich and Plumstead, and for Elementary kids from anywhere.

Part of Eltham Hill School, 1990; just as it looked in 1940

Next day I turned up at the school and found, guess what? Old 'Spotty' Prince. You didn't tell me he had left Deal. I sometimes wonder if you really are going to school down there. Prince, being the hopeless teacher he is, lined us up and unlined us for about half an hour, yelling and shouting all the time, trying to form us up into classes. None of us paid any attention as we were all too busy wandering around trying to catch up on all the latest news. There was Jones, Keating, Hammerfield from our class, plus two girls, Alma Evans and Margaret Radford. Alma kept on giggling when I asked her about you. What did you do to her? There are plenty of other kids I don't know. One seems a good sort. His name is Shaw and he cheeked Prince and got a smack across the face for his trouble. It seemed just like old times.

Our classroom is in a Science lab. The Head is a grim old sod called Haggar. I shall steer well clear of him. We won't be getting much sport because on the playing field there's a Barrage Balloon team of RAF men and women—the women are called Waafs. Haggar warned us not to go near the women. I don't know who he thought would be in danger because they're a tough lot and talk with funny accents. I think they're from Birmingham or somewhere like that up North.

We have no pens, no books, no paper and share one pencil between two. Dad says that with all this equipment we should be able to get down to some serious work. I've decided that Haggar is an idiot. He keeps on talking about preparing for later life by taking Matric. With one pencil between two! I ask you. How's your schooling going? Shall I ask Alma? She obviously knows a lot about you. (Swinehund). Write soon,

Cheerio,
Bill

57, St. Mary's Road,
Deal, Kent.
3rd December 1939

Dear Bill,

If you're in the same class as Alma, watch out!! In the Barretts of Wimpole Street, she was playing Elizabeth, who spends most of her time lying on a couch because she's an invalid. As Robert, I had to bend down and pick her up. Well, the first time I did it, her skirt must have got caught and as I lifted her up, there was I holding her bare thigh!!! She just smiled at me and pretended there was nothing wrong. But after the same thing happened at the next two rehearsals I suddenly realised that she was doing it deliberately. So, at the next rehearsal, once I'd picked her up and she was smiling sweetly at me as though nothing was wrong, I started to slide my hand up her thigh. She went bright red, and boy, did she wriggle!! So I dropped her. Right on her backside. And when Mrs Boon said it was all her own fault for not keeping still, I couldn't help smiling. And that's ALL that happened between Alma and me. If she says I love her, she's a liar. But you watch out for her, Bill. She's trouble.

The weather down here is awful. Wind, rain, gales and storms all the time. The Walmer lifeboat keeps on going out to rescue ships that have been mined or run aground. As they can't show any lights it's a wonder they manage to find anyone in such rough seas—and of course there's always the danger that they'll hit a mine themselves. One of the lifeboat men told me he knew the sea so well, he could smell where he was. Walter says he was pulling my leg, but I think he really meant it. I've experimented by closing my eyes and smelling my way around Deal. Unfortunately I keep on bumping into lamp-posts. Perhaps it's easier at sea.

Old Grindle told us in Assembly that next term we'll be back to working full time because we'll have the school all to ourselves. This joyful news was met with dead silence. Then that fool Walter started to clap—until I dug him sharply in the ribs. Ronnie Johnson, who as you know quickly finds out about these things, says it's because they are going to evacuate all the Deal schoolkids to somewhere safer. The way things are going, it wouldn't surprise me if they all end up in Eltham.

We've been away three months now and I'm beginning to really miss Mum and Dad. Of course I can't tell them that, as it would only upset them. I expect you'll be having one of your big family Christmas parties as usual. They say we should have plenty of snow down here, so at least that's something to look forward to. Write soon.

Your friend,
Merv

7, Nesbit Road,
Eltham, S.E.9.
2nd January 1940

Dear Merv,

Happy New Year, old bean! I told Roberts, that it was so long since I'd last seen you, I'd begun to forget what you looked like. He reckoned I was very, very lucky.

Did you have a good Christmas? I must say I felt sorry for you for the first time since the war began, not being at home and all that. Just before Christmas I popped around to Kenward Road to give your mum and dad a Christmas card. I think they are missing you too, although they didn't actually say so. They said you didn't write very often. I hadn't the heart to tell them that you were too busy sending me war communiques. Which reminds me, thanks for the warning about Alma. I think her backside is better now. She certainly wiggles it a lot!!!

It's freezing cold here, but we had a good family Christmas at my Aunt Ada's house in Plumstead. All my strange uncles and aunts were there with their children, John, Ken, Ron and Brenda who are great fun. Cousin John was evacuated to Ashford in Kent but he's back now and will be going to my school. We heard the King's broadcast about talking to the man at the gate of the year, which went down well.

The children of Bill's 'strange uncles and aunts'—
Ron, Elaine, Ken, John and Brenda with 'Aunt Ada'

The uncles—still playing cards after the war!

28

They've got copies of it stuck up in Montagu Burton's window in the High Street.

My grandfather, who fought in the Boer War, and dad who fought in the Great War, get a lot of amusement from the war bulletins on the radio, because the only raids we seem to carry out are not to drop bombs—but leaflets telling the Germans to give up. I ask you! This is the army that took us four years to beat last time. Grandad's favourite bulletin is, 'A lorry was seen to overturn'. He says they could have done that in the Boer War before aeroplanes were invented.

We played Aunt Ada's favourite game—Nuts in May—which has a lot of tugging in it and as John and Ken are as big as me, was a lot of fun. All my uncles sat for hours and hours playing cards, then spent just as long arguing over who laid the wrong trump and all that sort of rot. But on Christmas morning I was allowed to go round to the Nag's Head with the men. Just as we'd started to really enjoy ourselves, Aunt Ada marched in and mucked it all up saying that dinner was waiting. When I'm grown up no woman's going to drag me out of a pub.

Dad reckons this 'phoney war', as they call it, won't last much longer and says that when it really does start, it'll be worse than last time and take six years, not four. He says that all we seem to have at the moment is an army of crooners singing, 'We're going to hang out our washing on the Siegfried Line'. Two of my uncles are young enough to be called up. I wonder if they'll be with us next Christmas?

Back home, I went on writing my life of Napoleon. I'm up to the Battle of Wagram in 1809, so there's still a lot to do. The exercise book situation is terrible. At school we've only been using sheets of paper. If I tried to smuggle any of it out of school, Haggar would enjoy skinning me alive because he's already taken a dislike to me. He says I'm big-headed. I know I am, but unlike him, I've got something to be big-headed about. After all, where's his life of Napoleon?

Cheerio. Write soon.

Bill

57, St. Mary's Road,
Deal, Kent.
12th January 1940

Dear Bill,

You watch out for Alma and her wriggling backside. I sent her a Christmas card, only I didn't sign it, just wrote, 'Happy Landings'. Say to her, 'This is Funf speaking. Haf you had any gute Christmas cards?' Then she'll know that you know.

Mum and Dad were going to come down just before Christmas but at the last moment they couldn't manage it. They really wanted to and were very disappointed, only Dad's just been made foreman at the factory so he couldn't take the time off. But they did send me a parcel. Mum and Dad gave me a penknife, a Boys Own Annual and a pair of leather gloves— the gauntlet type that despatch riders have—and Vev and Eric sent me thirty shillings! I'm still working out what to buy with it.

Christmas with the Pyms was very good but it wasn't the same as being at home. We had chicken, Christmas pudding and elderberry wine!! And we were even going to pour brandy over the pudding and light it, only Auntie Kitty drank it all while she was cooking the dinner, which was a great pity as I've never seen that done before. Auntie Freddie got quite angry, but Kitty just giggled and started to sing, 'One Day When We Were Young' then fell asleep on the sofa. So, Auntie Freddie said to me, what's good for the goose and got a bottle of SLOE GIN out of the sideboard. By golly, Bill you want to try some. It's good strong stuff. I even had half of Walter's glass because he fell asleep on the sofa as well. Freddie made me keep some back to toast the King on the radio. At home, Dad always switches him off and never stands up for the National Anthem, even at the pictures. He used to belong to the Industrial World Workers, which is against kings and all that sort of thing, so I suppose it just became a habit.

What about all this snow and ice? We had some good snow battles at the beginning but now no one bothers much. There was a rumour going round that they were going to close the school. I asked Ronnie

Johnson if it was true but he said it wouldn't happen. I felt so depressed, I wished I hadn't asked him.

Old Dickie Bird is still as useless as ever. The other day in the science lab, he was flapping around trying to make himself heard as we were all busy talking, so he shouts out at the top of his squeaky voice, 'Every time I open my mouth all I can hear is some damned fool talking'. And the idiot couldn't understand why we started laughing. Anyway, that's not the end of the story. He gathered us around the bench and said that the experiment he was about to perform was extremely dangerous and that the last time, it had all blown up. So he mixes the chemicals, lights a match and the whole bloody thing does blow up!!! We were still rolling on the floor laughing when they carted him off to the First Aid Centre.

The only other bit of good news was that I did get to play Papa Barrett in the end. After Alma went, Mrs Boon changed us all around. Joan Longley played Elizabeth and will surely become a great film star one day. My old part of Robert was played by Johnny Jackson. He wasn't very good and kept forgetting his words. He even tried to make an exit through a window which was supposed to be on the first floor! I used two pillows to make myself look fat and shouted so loud that one of the first formers started to cry. Afterwards he said that I'd sounded just like his Dad, which I think was the nicest compliment I could have been given.

We still hear the odd explosion but nothing of what you would call 'historical importance' has happened. But if there is any machine-gunning or bombing, I promise to let you know, providing I'm not dead. Ronnie Johnson has just called and says he can borrow a tobogan, so we're off to have some fun. I'll post this on the way. He's also told me that Mrs Boon is going back to London, so she could turn up at your end. Ronnie says it was because of my performance. Anyway, I thought you ought to be warned.

Your friend,

Merv

7, Nesbit Road,
Eltham, S.E.9.
25th January 1940

Dear Merv,

I know Mrs Boon is back in London! She turned up at the school grinning like a Cheshire cat. As if that wasn't bad enough, she then went around SHAKING HANDS with all the pupils she remembered. I ask you, what a daft thing to do! I don't know about you, but I've never shaken a woman's hand before. It was all weak and clammy. When I was younger, my aunts used to kiss me on the cheek, which left it all wet. Of course foreigners spend all their time kissing cheeks and shaking hands, but then they are foreigners. Dad laughed when I moaned about it and said that if I only shook hands with women I wouldn't come to much harm. I said he didn't know Mrs Boon.

Haggar decided to make us take turns at Bible readings at Assembly. I didn't mind because I like reading aloud. But guess what happened? I had the most rotten luck! I had to read out the name 'Beezlebub'. I'd never come across it before, so I pronounced it, 'Beezle-bub'—get it? Haggar hit the roof and accused me of making fun of the Bible. Said it should be pronounced, 'BE-L-ZEEBUB' and then the swine caned me!! I ask you. I don't mind suffering if I've done something wrong, but I was INNOCENT. I got one on each hand because of that rotten, bloody name. It's quite obvious that Haggar hates me because of my Life of Napoleon.

As you can imagine, I felt very sore—in every way— about this injustice. After all, what are we supposed to be fighting against in this war but injustice and tyranny? And Alma didn't help. She passed me a note saying how unfair that I should be punished for my ignorance! I could have hit her! I bet she couldn't have said Beezlebub either. In fact, I bet it was the first time she'd even heard of this bloody fallen angel!!

My grandad hasn't been too well lately. I overheard dad say he had dropsy, so I went to the hospital to see him. A nurse took me along to the ward and when we got there the bed was empty. When dad had phoned from the call-box half an hour before, they said, 'There was no

32

change'. No change?! They didn't even know he'd left. And I get caned for saying a word wrong!!

Back at his house in Welling, grandad and I had a long talk about the Boer War. He had some interesting old magazines called, 'With the flag to Pretoria'. He told me that at the Battle of Paardeberg, the Boers kept them lying face down in the grass for hours with their accurate rifle fire. He said that they were so good, that if you even put a finger up, a bullet would either whistle near it or take it clean off. On top of that, they had repeating rifles while the poor old British were still using the single-shot Martini-Henry. I asked him about the hospital.

Courtesy of African Museum, Johannesburg, S.A.

'Some interesting old magazines called, *With the Flag to Pretoria*'. British soldiers during the Boer War, 1899-1902

He said if he was going to die it was going to be in his own bed, so he put a coat on over his pyjamas, walked out and caught the bus home. Through all that snow! What a family I was born into!

Today is mum's birthday. She's made herself a cake which I expect dad and I will eat. She had to save up a lot of the sugar ration but it looks as though it was worth it. Dad's found a single candle and is about to light it.

Cheerio,
Bill

57, St.Mary's Road,
Deal, Kent.
9th February 1940

Dear Bill,

At long last something historical has happened! I expect you'll say it's not all that important, but I bet you'll end up putting it in your diary. This is good stuff.

Two nights ago, we were all woken up by a tremendous explosion. (Aunt Kitty claims it was so great it threw her on the floor, but according to Aunt Freddie, she just dived under the bed.) Anyway, by the time Walter and I got to our window, there was nothing to see but blackness. Then there was another explosion, not nearly as loud as the first one, sort of muffled. That's when we saw her. She was a cargo ship and not very far out at sea. The second explosion must have come from inside the ship and set fire to something, because now we could see flames and the sailors were starting to lower a boat. The sea was very rough and there was a strong wind which was blowing the ship towards the shore. Then the flames died down and for a long while we couldn't see anything. We didn't know what had happened at all.

We must have stood looking out of the window for a good half hour. We were freezing and we were just about to go back to bed when Walter spotted the ship again. He must have good eyesight because I could hardly see it. In that half hour she'd drifted and we'd been looking in the wrong place because now she was almost on the beach. We couldn't see any men on board, so I suppose they got away in the boats or were picked up by the Walmer lifeboat. Anyway, it looked as though she was coming right up on to the beach, but at the last moment she suddenly swung around and headed for the pier. Then, as some big waves caught her, she gathered speed and started to smash herself against the pier. And that's when Aunt Kitty came up and made us go back to bed. Even Walter said that was a rotten thing to do.

We stayed awake for a long time, listening to the ship as she kept on bashing into the pier. Even with all the wind we could hear this grinding and groaning sound. It was very weird. The next morning I got up early for once—and lucky I did because I saw it all happen. By now, the pier had started to sag and the sea suddenly pulled the ship away from it—just like it had been doing all night—only this time the ship went right through the pier, cutting it clean in half! Once she was through to the other side, she sort of gave up, rolled over on her side and ran aground on the beach. Her name is NORA. Trust a woman to smash a pier in half. You wouldn't get The Rodney or The Prince of Wales doing a daft thing like that!

The *Nora* after she had smashed through the Deal pier

After breakfast, we went down on the beach. There were lots of people there, just standing looking at the wreck. They needn't have bothered taking planks out of the pier— the Nora's made a much better job of it.

No one really knew exactly what happened, but most people thought she'd hit a mine and then her engine room had blown up. Later on, when the tide came in, we found hundreds and hundreds of pencils washed up on the beach. Nothing exciting like guns or grenades—just pencils! I ask you Bill, what sort of wartime cargo is that for a ship to be carrying? If you write about this in that famous diary of yours, you could say, 'As described by our War Correspondent'—only make sure you give my name as well, so that people will know it's me.

Came across another piece of history last week. Aunt Freddie took us for a ride in the countryside. The car was an Austin Ruby and the owner was a man called Bruno something-or-other. He said as he didn't really need to use the car, it would help the war effort if he gave up his petrol ration and laid it up for the duration. This was going to be the last run in it until the end of the war.

When we got home, Freddie told us the real reason. Bruno had been born in Germany and he'd heard that all foreigners were going to be locked up. So he was getting everything neat and tidy for the day when they would come and cart him off. For a German he seemed quite nice, but I expect that's because he's lived in England for so long.

Anyway, this is the important bit. While we were driving around, we came across the grave of Lord French of Ypres. It was a very funny feeling to suddenly come across the name Ypres written on a stone in the middle of Kent. You'd have liked it. It was quite historical. Bet you didn't know he was buried down here. None of us did.

What about those Russian swine attacking poor little Finland? They're as bad as the Nazis. Aunt Freddie says that once we've beaten the Germans, we'll have to go on and beat the Russians as well. She gets quite angry about the war and thumps the table just like my Dad. She's got no time for Chamberlain and says the only thing he's good at is giving away other people's countries.

Sunday is the only day we all have breakfast together. While Aunt Kitty is clearing away, Aunt Freddie pours herself another big mug of tea, lights up a Capstain and starts a discussion—only it's an argument really. The game is, that whatever she says, we've got to argue against it. Walter is useless. He either says nothing or agrees with everything she says. I'm quite used to it, because at home we have an argument every Sunday. Dad's very good at switching things. Just when you think you're winning, you find that somehow he's got you on to another subject. I've tried that trick on Aunt Freddie, only she won't let me get away with it. But it doesn't matter whether it's politics, religion or films, it always ends up the same, with Freddie and me shouting at one another, Walter suddenly remembering he's got a letter to write, and Kitty saying she's either got a headache or that she needs the table to do the vegetables. I like Sundays.

How are you getting on with the food rationing? I'm glad we'd already given up sugar because that means we can still have cakes and puddings and things. I expect you've finished that birthday cake by now? I wonder if Kitty will make me one next month? My birthday's on the fifteenth!

School still goes on. All we ever seem to do in French, is write out pages and pages of verbs—which is not much help when you don't even know what the words mean. We've got a new English teacher called Miss Pitts. Of course, with a name like that, she was nicknamed Zazu on her first day. She's got thin lips and looks like a witch. I don't think I'm going to like her. We start on the Merchant of Venice next week. If she chooses me to play Shylock I might change my mind about her. My pen's running out of ink and I'm not going up to the bedroom to fill it again because it's freezing up there, so will close now.

Your friend,

Merv

7, Nesbit Road,
Eltham, S.E.9.
24th February 1940

Dear Merv,

Stop arguing with Freddie. Arguing with women is a waste of time dad says. And with all his sisters he should know.

Thanks very much for your stirring tale of the pier at Deal. Whether it will affect the course of world history or not I don't know, but it certainly sounds exciting. This is more than can be said about London—where all the bombing was supposed to be!

I don't know what an Austin Ruby looks like, except that it's a car. As you know we are a motor-bike family. Just before the war, dad saved up and bought a Francis Barnett 150cc two stroke, on the never-never. You may remember seeing it when we lived up at Alnwick Road? The bike could only carry one passenger, so dad used to take mum and myself for rides in the country by relay. First, he would take mum to Farningham and leave her on a seat in the village. Then he

Bill's mother just before the war

'Miss Wilcox'

38

would drive back and pick me up. Mum then went on to Sutton-at-Hone and I was left on the seat—and so it went on. We had one really smashing ride. It was November 5th. Mum was at home, and as we came back in the dark, there were fireworks lighting up the sky all around us. I'll always remember that. In the end dad couldn't afford to keep up the weekly payments and had to sell it. He really did like that Francis Barnett. That was just before we came to live in Nesbit Road.

We sometimes talk about car rides. My grandad says the one way to be sure of a ride in a car during a General Election, is to tell the local Tory canvasser that you're going to vote Conservative! That way you get a free lift to the Polling Station. Grandad's only been in a car three times in his life, and they were all during General Elections. Come to think of it, the only election you and I really remember was in 1936 when Kingsley Wood won this seat for the Tories. Do you remember all the cars floating about with their loud-speakers blaring? Baldwin and the Tories got in. I expect your dad was as furious as mine.

You ask about rationing. It doesn't affect us too much because my Uncle Charley, Aunt Ada's husband, runs a grocery stall in Beresford Square market and a shop at Welling. So now and again there is some off the ration food knocking about. We don't get as much as some of the family because dad and Uncle Charley have never got on all that well. Still, he does pop in now and again with some extras. We also get school dinners. Do you? It seems strange to stay at school during the dinner hour instead of walking home for a meal. But Mum just hasn't got the food to feed both me and dad anymore, so that's why I stay.

Haggar seems to like school dinners. He makes us say 'Grace' before we eat. We don't do anything like that at home. Just thank Mum when we've finished.

Dad wouldn't let me go to Sunday school or become a Cub in case I turned Christian. I expect your father felt the same. I certainly can't remember you going to the Cub Hut off Court Road. Anyway, once we've prayed, we all have to sit and eat in silence. Anybody who talks gets lines. The girls get in an awful state because they're such gossips. Have you noticed how girls can't stop talking? I don't mind being quiet, especially when I think of Haggar's cane. The trouble is, we are so silent it makes us giggle. Last week Haggar threatened to cane Parkes for giggling and the only reason he didn't was that several girls were giggling at the same time. So in a way, I'm rather thankful we're in a mixed school—otherwise I think Haggar would spend all his time caning every boy he could lay his hands on. I wonder if he got a degree in caning?

I can't understand why the Finns are doing so well against the Russians. After all, think of the size of the two countries. Perhaps it's because the Russians can't ski as well? The newsreels show men in white whizzing in and out of trees or firing at nothing in particular. Dad says that these photographs are fakes. He said that during the Great War, men were told to lay down and pretend to fire at the enemy—even though they were miles behind the lines. The reason was, that the cameras were much too big and heavy to be used in the front line. He says that he's seen the same picture used in totally different battles. So keep an eye open. They've got plenty of film of the war in China. You might see the Japs or Chinese fighting in Finland.

French verbs don't worry me like they do you. I told our French teacher, Mr Budge, that English was a far richer language. This was why Shakespeare used it. He replied that Shakespeare used it because he was English not French. I argued back, and the whole lesson went by without a single verb being written down, let alone learnt! Then Budge had a bright idea. He asked me why, if I despised French so much, was I writing the life of Napoleon. I said it was because Napoleon was really an Italian from Corsica. This nearly got me into real trouble. Budge didn't know anything about Napoleon and thought I was being cheeky. I just managed to convince him before he called Haggar. Quite tricky really. If he had called Haggar, I doubt that he would have known enough about Napoleon to realise I was speaking the truth. That's the trouble with being taught by ignorant teachers!!

I think you will be playing Shylock. Anybody who's too mean or lazy to go upstairs to fill his pen should play Shylock (I'm only joking). Do you remember when we played Old and Young Gobbo in that concert? Ah, happy days! I wish you were with us now instead of living with women who smoke all the time and roll about under beds. Your 'Zasu' Pitts doesn't sound a patch on our new English teacher. Her name is Miss Wilcox and I think she taught at Woolwich Central before the war. She is a socialist and is really clever. She read one of my essays and said I'd got real talent. Now there's a smart lady for you!

I'd better stop writing after that. You might travel all the way from Deal just to scrag me.

Cheerio,

Bill

P.S. What about the 'Cossack' getting all those prisoners off the 'Altmark'? One of the prisoners, a merchant navy captain, lives in Glenelg Road. The Kentish Independent reporters have been hanging around his house, which as you know, is quite near the school. They want to ask him about life on the Altmark and the Graf Spee. In our family, the local papers are always known as the 'Plum Pudding Press', because years ago grandad read letter after letter, for week after week, all about the different ways to make plum puddings. Now the Plum Pudding Press will have something historic to write about for a change!

57, St.Mary's Road,
Deal, Kent.
12th March 1940

Dear Bill,

I wish you hadn't reminded me about us playing Launcelot and Gobbo. Do you know what part Zasu Pitts has got me reading? Bassanio! About the soppiest part in the play. At least with Launcelot I could have had some fun. All Bassanio does, is borrow money from his friend so that he can pretend he's wealthy when he goes after Portia, so that he can marry her and get his greedy hands on all her money to pay off his debts. I said to Miss Pitts that I reckoned he was

41

the real villain and asked if I could play him like Basil Rathbone. She told me not to be stupid and concentrate on my iambic pentameter. Your Miss Wilcox has got to be better than her!

Gussy Arkwright's reading Shylock and making a proper muck up of it. He doesn't sound a bit Jewish. I told him to listen to Maxie Bacon on the radio, but I don't suppose he will.

Went to see 'The Lion Has Wings' at the Fleapit last Saturday. Johnny Jackson showed Ronnie Johnson and me how to get in for nothing. Well, almost nothing. We sent Walter in first with a ninepenny ticket. (Do you know he's getting 3/- a week pocket money now?) You need to time it just right. At the interval, when everyone goes to the bog, he went along too—only first he went to the exit door, which is always by the bog, and slipped the catch. Once we were in, he told us which seats were empty. All we had to do was pick up an old ticket stub in case one of the usherettes asked to see it. See how easy it is? It would work a treat at Eltham Palace. If you charged six of your mates tuppence each, you'd even have a joey left for yourself for an icecream.

Walter said he wasn't going to do it again because his father worked in a bank and if we were caught his Dad could lose his job. We all agreed that if he felt like that, it wouldn't be right for us to pay him back our share of the ninepence. That got him properly upset.

I've never really thought that much about money before, but when I wrote to Mum to ask if I could have more pocket money, she said they were now having to pay the government 6/- a week towards my keep. I'm sure I can't eat that much food in a week! It's probably all going to pay for your school dinners. We don't have anything like that down here.

The other day I saw some ships way out at sea and each one was flying a barrage balloon. I can't think why, unless they hoped bombs would bounce off them. But it did give me an idea. If you had a balloon big enough, it could lift a ship right out of the water when there was a danger of it being torpedoed. That would fool the U-Boats.

Apart from Nora, the pier and the black-out, you wouldn't know there was a war on down here. I think the next time I write home, I'll suggest to Mum that they bring me back to Eltham. After all, it's costing them six shillings a week. If I did come back, they could even afford to increase my pocket money to 2/6 and they'd still be five bob a week better off.

Anyway, I'll let you know what happens.

Your friend,
Merv

7, Nesbit Road,
Eltham, S.E.9.
26th March 1940

Dear Merv,

I was right about Miss Wilcox. She's a first class teacher. Not pretty, but handsome, with nice legs which she crosses as she sits on the desk to talk to us. We boys get a good view now and again. The trouble is, she lisps a lot and if you get too near you get showered. Anyway, she's set us to work on the De Coverley Papers. I don't suppose you've ever heard of them? I hadn't until a week ago. They are essays for a newspaper called 'The Spectator' and were written by two men called Addison and Steele. The fun is to spot which man wrote which, as they wrote in different ways. Some are quite funny. Miss Wilcox makes them come alive by telling us stories about them. Apparently, Addison wrote a poem about the Battle of Blenheim. I must try to get hold of a copy as I'm very interested in Marlborough's battles, as you know. I shall try to copy Addison's style in my letters, so look out for some pretty breath-taking stuff.

You know I used to muck about playing the spoons? Well, dad's bought me some proper ivory clappers and I'm trying to play them as well as my Uncle Jim. He's a wizard with them and at Christmas parties plays all the old cockney tunes like 'Boiled Beef and Carrots'. I rattle away as dad plays his mandolin. As you know, he's a first class player. He used to play in a jazz band on the Orient liner 'Orsova' during trips to Australia and back. This was just after I was born. The

43

Bill's father on deck of *Orsova* off the coast of Australia, April 1928

tunes are a bit out of date, being popular in the twenties and early thirties, but I like to hear dad play them.

Dad says he ran away to sea when I was born because he couldn't stand my crying. Of course the real reason he went to sea was because he couldn't get a job on land. He'd been out of work for years. It still makes him very bitter, especially as he fought in the war. You have to keep him off 'A land fit for heroes to live in'. He still hates Lloyd George because of that slogan.

I suppose you know that my real name is not Bill but Laurence—or perhaps you'd forgotten. I was named after my dad's bosom friend in the army, Laurence O'Hare. The trouble was, he forgot that this same O'Hare had jilted my Aunt Agnes. At least, that's what she reckoned. Anyway, all the other aunts took offence and refused to call me Laurence. That's why I ended up as Bill, which I like better. Dad tried to get around it by telling them he'd named me after D.H.Lawrence who is one of his favourite authors. They didn't believe him because it's spelt differently—which only goes to prove that at least one of them can read. Mum says it was because dad started burbling 'Billikin, Billikin' at me in my pram. Now he calls me 'The Guvnor', though I can't think why. He says it's because I lay the law down—but then so do all my family!!

Bill's father at Cawnpore, India, in 1921. The 'Laurence' Bill was named after is on his left

Shaw and I went to see Charlton play Brentford at the Valley last week. It now costs 6d to get in!!! It may make you home-sick, but things haven't changed since we used to go before the war. Sammy Bartram still folds his cap and puts it in the corner of the goal until the sun shines, and he can still clear the pitch with a goal kick—which is a bit of a waste of time really although he's a wonderful goalie. Hobbis, the winger, is still called 'Obbis' by the crowd and Oakes's bald head is still as popular as ever. The Brentford lot were really dirty players. Twice they brought down Hobbis with foul tackles. The man next to me got really annoyed because he said everyone knew that Obbis had brittle legs and if Brentford did it again, he'd personally go down and break a few of their legs.

The crowd still shouts, 'Keep it on the island' and everyone who goes is an expert—including the women. They're all so good at giving advice, they must all be ex-internationals at least. One thing did happen which made everyone laugh. A man ran onto the pitch! I thought at first that he was a trainer or a doctor, but no, he was a spectator. I think he was probably drunk because he took his glasses off and insisted on giving them to the ref. A policeman chased him and soon carted him off. Oh, by the way, Charlton won 3-2.

After the match, we all filed through that tunnel which leads on to the Greenwich Road. How we all got through without being crushed to death I'll never know. All the trams were full up but Shaw and I had gone on bikes. Even so, the road was so crowded we couldn't cycle. I reckon at least eight thousand of us walked back to Woolwich. There was a lot of moaning about the Brentford players but most of it was good humoured—probably because we won. Shaw says we ought to try to get to Arsenal. Their bad language is even worse, and the Arsenal supporters are even more expert. There's absolutely nothing they don't know about football!!

Grandad is much worse, I'm afraid. He's been taken to the Miller hospital. Dad and the rest of the family take turns to go and see him. I've been twice. They seem to be draining water out of his side, so I suppose it's dropsy. He's very brave and chats away as though nothing is wrong. My aunts just cry, so they're no use at all. Dad and he swap stories about their old regiment, the Rifle Brigade.

Has Deal got a football team? I doubt it. Still, it has got a lifeboat which is more than Eltham has!

Cheerio,
Bill

57, St. Mary's Road,
Deal, Kent.
15th April 1940

Dear Laurence,

No, no, somehow Laurence doesn't sound right. I think I'll stick to Bill. I've never told you this before—and don't laugh—but I was damned nearly christened Christopher Robin. That soppy song about a boy saying his prayers was all the rage at the time. Thank God Mum listened to the Welsh nurse at the hospital and called me Mervyn instead. As you know I'm not afraid of a scrap, but with a name like Christopher Robin I'd have ended up in a fight every day of my life. My second name's Oliver, after Sir Oliver Lodge. He was a spiritualist. Mum and Dad went into spiritualism for a bit after Stella died. That was before I was born. I think they had me as a replacement.

Dad and Mum came down last Sunday on the coach. They were worried by my letter suggesting I should come home. First thing Dad did, was to go to the house to look-over the Misses Pym. While we were waiting for Freddie in the front room, Dad saw they had books by Jack London and H.G. Wells, his favourite writers. Then, when he found three books by Engels, he told me I was in good hands—and that was even before he'd met Freddie. The two of them got on like a house on fire and I was left sitting in a corner while they talked politics. Kitty brought in mugs of tea and cakes and Freddie chain-smoked until you could hardly see across the room. Dad was most impressed when Freddie told him how she'd nearly gone off to Spain to fight against Franco. And Freddie was just as impressed when Dad told her he was a founder member of the I.W.W. He even showed her a badge that he

47

Mervyn's mother with Eric, Vevlie and Stella long before he was born. Stella is on the left

wears on the back of his lapel. After that we went for a walk along the front.

It was a funny sort of day. Dad and I really talked. About all kinds of things. He told me lots about himself and his family that I never knew before. We'd gone along towards Walmer and got ourselves between a couple of boats that had been pulled up on the beach. It was out of the wind and as Dad said, 'we were as snug as bugs in a rug'. That's one of his favourite sayings.

It all started when he asked me what I wanted to do when I left school. I said I didn't know and asked him what engineering was like. That's when he really began to talk. Dad started his training when he was thirteen and did a seven year apprenticeship with Aveling and Porters, who make steam rollers and engines. He'd really wanted to be an artist and his headmaster at the Mathematical School in Rochester pleaded with grandfather to send him to an art school—so he must have been good. But the old man said no. He was an engineer and all his sons were going to be engineers. Only the eldest boy was allowed to choose what he wanted to do. That was my Uncle Bertie. He went to sea, sailed the world before the mast and ended up a captain.

My other two uncles, Jimmy and Seth, also became engineers only they emigrated to New Zealand and Canada. Dad had another brother, but he fell into a copper of boiling water when he was three and died. There was also Hartie, Maud and Lizzie, so they were quite a large family. They had a big house on Rochester Esplanade and even had a couple of servants.

He said Rochester was a smashing place when he was a boy. There were lots of sailing barges on the river then, and men in rowing boats used to wait and go aboard to take them through the narrow arches of the old bridge. They had to line the boat up just right and at the last moment, the sails and masts came down and the barge shot through the bridge with only inches to spare. They were real experts and were called 'bridge hufflers'.

Dad said Saturday nights were the best. He and all his brothers and sisters would put on their Sunday clothes for a night out on the town.

49

Mervyn's grandfather, Josiah Seth Haisman

His sisters would sometimes stuff a coil of rope up the back of their skirts to make it look as though they had bustles. They could always get into the music hall at the Theatre Royal because one of their uncles was the manager. He was very strict and wouldn't allow men into the theatre unless they wore a collar—even in the gallery. But he made sure everyone got in because he sold them cardboard collars for a halfpenny. The Theatre Royal was in Chatham and on a Saturday night, there were always lots of fights between the Navy, Army and Marines stationed there.

One of my Uncle's favourite tricks was to send my father, who was the youngest, around the corner to poke fun at some of the young men—only he called them 'mashers'. They'd then chase Dad back around the corner where his brothers were waiting to slap dollops of peas-pudding in their faces. Dad couldn't stop laughing when he told me about it. But I bet if I tried that trick today, I'd either be expelled or sent to a Reform School.

Dad's grandfather was called Barnabus and he was quite rich. He owned several ships and a whole street of houses in Rochester, but his

Mervyn's great-grandfather,
Barnabus Seth Baldwin Haisman

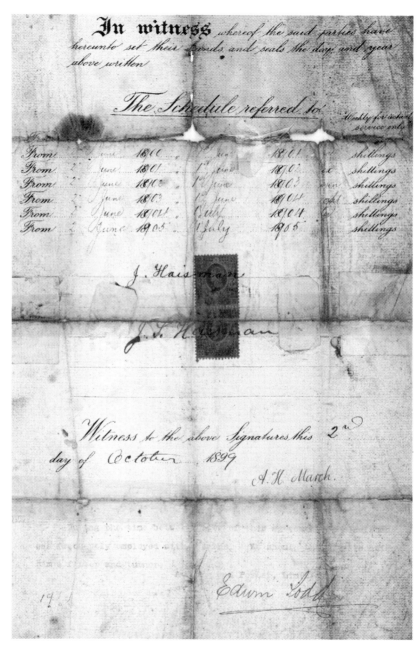

In witness whereof the said parties have hereunto set their hands and seals the day and year above written

The Schedule referred to

Weekly for actual service only

From						
From	June	1800	June	1801		shillings
From	June	1801	June	1802		shillings
From	June	1802	June	1803		shillings
From	June	1803	June	1804		shillings
From	June	1804	July	1804		shillings
From	June	1805	July	1805		shillings

J. Haisman

J. T. Haisman

Witness to the above Signatures this 2nd day of October 1899

A. H. March.

Edwin Todd

Mervyn's father's Articles of Indenture for his apprenticeship

52

downfall was women. Every time he had a new lady-friend, he'd sell a house. He must have had an awful lot of lady-friends because the only thing he left was the house on the Esplanade. He died when he was ninetyone, trying to jump a five-bar gate. He bet someone he could do it. He lost.

On the way back to the house Dad told me that when he was an apprentice, engineers were highly respected and could work anywhere in the world. As part of his training he even had to make his own micrometer. He said that then, engineers could turn their hand to anything. But all that changed with mass-production. The skill wasn't needed. During the slump, he and Uncle Seth went to America to look for work. They travelled steerage and ended up working at Fords in Detroit. As soon as he'd saved up enough money he came back, only by then the slump was worse than ever. Dad said that over the years he'd lost a lot of jobs because he was always the one who stood up to the bosses. He'd get the sack and his mates would go on working.

We had a smashing Sunday dinner and then it was time to go for the coach. On the way, I plucked up courage and told Dad that I didn't want to be an engineer. What I really wanted to be, was an actor. He didn't say anything for quite a long while, then he said, 'Well, why not? I don't know how you're going to do it, but you prove to me that you've got the ability, and I'll stand by you.' That made me feel good, only now I think about it, I've no idea of how I can become an actor. But it's what I really want to be.

After he'd gone, I went for a long walk and thought about all he'd said. We've never talked like that before. I suppose it's because I'm growing up. I'm glad I've written all this down as it's helped me to remember.

I've just read your last letter again. Yes, you going to Charlton did make me homesick. I expect my brother Eric was there too. Most Saturdays he'd be following his own club, Middle Park, which he formed in 1928, but when the war came they decided to pack up for the duration. Stupid really, because for all that's happened, they could still be playing.

53

Middle Park Football Club on a charabanc outing. Eric, front row, far right

In 1938 they won the Brockley League and Eric brought the cup home and proudly put it on the sideboard in the front room. Mum got fed up with it. She said it was alright for Eric to bring all his friends in to admire it, but she was the one who had to clean it every week.

Was your account of the match meant to be in the style of Addison? I only ask, because if it was, I couldn't notice the difference.

Sorry to hear about your grandfather. I hope he gets better. Aunt Kitty has told me three times to go to bed, so will close now.

Your friend,

Merv

Dear Merv,

Sorry I've not written for some time but I'm afraid grandad has died. Mum and dad were at the pictures in Lewisham when a policeman called at the house to tell me that he was very ill at the Miller hospital. I cycled frantically to Lewisham and persuaded the commissionaire to put a sign up on the film, which was some sob-stuff with Norma Shearer in it. Mum and dad came out and caught the tram straight to the hospital. I followed on my bike. When we got there, grandad was in a coma. He looked much smaller and withered, as though he was dead already. Dad pointed to a scar on grandad's forehead. He told me that he had hit grandad with a kitchen poker in a fight they'd had when he was on leave during the Great War. Both of them were drunk at the time. Now dad felt bad about it.

Three days later grandad died. Granny had the body brought back to the house at Welling. His face looked just like it was wax, only as the

Bill's mother's grave; she died in 1947. The grave of his grandfather is a few yards away

55

weather got hot it began to go green. I heard my aunts whispering about whether they should put the lid on. They thought I couldn't hear. Next day the undertakers came and shut him down.

Yesterday, I went to my first funeral. As the vicar said, 'Ashes to ashes, dust to dust,' I thought how fitting it would be to sound the Last Post. After all, he was a brave soldier and I shall miss our little talks about the Boer War. I don't think my aunts really care much that he's gone. They seemed frightened of him at times, though I know for a fact that he never hit them.

He was a tough man who grew up in the streets of London as an orphan. He was the chucker-out and potman at the Red Lion, yet he was also a clever, well-read man. Did I ever tell you that he knew Robert Tressall, the man who wrote 'The Ragged Trousered Philantropist'? Your father, with his 'red' politics, would have heard of that book, I expect.

We had end of term football with the Elementary scruffs. Woe of woes!! We lost 3-0. Roberts fought like a lion and I repulsed dozens of attacks but it was no use. Our forwards were the weak spots. Of course, playing in the playground means you can bounce the ball off the wire and run round people, but it's hardly Arsenal stuff! The Waafs won't let us use the playing fields. They chase us off even if we peep at them—or threaten to tell Haggar. Even if you glare at a female, Haggar will cane you. He really will! If you have a row with a girl, it's you he canes. And if you get sent out of a class, he'll look through the glass and if it's a lady teacher, he'll lead you off for execution. Heard some of the teachers talking. It seems that Haggar is having an affair with Mrs Boon. Filthy old beast.

Mrs Boon took us for football because there are hardly any men teachers left who can move—let alone blow a whistle. She doesn't know a thing about the game and made us all run around—even if we were nowhere near the ball. She made Lee run around and he was the goalie! It got so bad that every time we kicked the ball, we aimed it straight at her. In the end we got her right in the bread-basket. When she collapsed we were all a bit worried, so we got the girls to take her to Haggar. He was hardly likely to cane them. After that we waited for an 'invitation' to his study, but it never came. I've got the feeling that Mrs Boon won't be taking football anymore.

Did you know that she writes a Woman's Page in a Sunday newspaper under the name of 'Aunt Alice'? I think I'll write a letter to her pretending to be a girl and see what she says. If the wheeze works, wait for my next letter. If I'm found out, you should hear my screams in Deal!!!

Cheerio,
Bill

57, St. Mary's Road,
Deal, Kent.
6th May 1940

Dear Bill,

Sorry to hear that your grandad died. I didn't know that dropsy was all that serious. I've never seen anyone dead. When Mum's Dad died I was only three and I don't think I saw the body. All I can remember is travelling through the night in a coach and waking up to see lots and lots of tall chimneys everywhere. It looked as though the sky was full of them. It was somewhere up north. I suppose I must have been taken to the funeral but I can't be sure. In fact, I can only just about remember Grandad Smith, because I think I only saw him twice before he died. He was a big man with a beard and a watch chain.

Grandad Smith was the Captain of the sailing barge Ventura. His first barge was called, Chalk. Mum often talks about him and what a wonderful man he was. He always took her with him whenever he could and there was a reason for this. She says that he came back from one trip to find his wife and three kids dead. It was the diptheria. After that, whenever he could, he took Mum with him. She says she'll always remember Sunday mornings at Greenwich. The river was quiet then and to see all the barges moored close together was quite a sight. Then the Mission barge would come alongside and everyone would put on their Sunday best and go aboard for a service. Grandad was a lay-

57

Mervyn's maternal grandfather, George J. Smith

preacher but he'd only give a sermon if the men asked him. Funny that— I've only just realised that Mum must have been quite religious when she was young. Now, she never goes to church. Something must have made her change.

Freddie has sold her dress shop. I asked her why, and she said it wasn't worth it anymore, what with all the shortages and everything and that it could only get worse. But something is going on! I heard her and Kitty quarreling. She told her that she was behaving like an ostrich and then said something about it being written on the wall. When I went into the kitchen later I had a good look round, but I couldn't see any writing. I suppose it must have been some other wall she was talking about.

Freddie says that now we've landed in Norway, things are going to hot up very soon. She reads three newspapers every day, so she knows an awful lot about everything. You can talk to Freddie. I told her my problem about not having enough pocket money. She asked me if I'd be willing to stay in and invest some of my pocket money in what she called 'a venture'. When I said yes, she went up to the loft and came down with a big box. There were lots of panes of glass and books of coloured silver paper. Then she showed me how to make silver paper pictures. It was a hobby of hers before the war.

I'm going to start on a crinoline lady, then I might do Donald Duck or the Seven Dwarfs. I've worked it all out. Paying for the paint, glue and passe-partout should come to threepence for every picture. This is where you come in. You can sell them for me in Eltham. I should think they'll easily go for 3/- each, but just to make sure they sound like a bargain, you can sell them for 2/11½ each. What do you think of the idea? If it works, it could just about save me. And providing you do your bit, I might even make a lot of money.

Your friend,
Merv

59

7, Nesbit Road,
Eltham, S.E.9.
12th May 1940

Dear Merv,

What price the war news? The Germans are up to their old tricks again. Last time it was Belgium. This time it's Holland and all points west. Dad reckons Norway was just a sideshow. They mean business this time! I told our history teacher, Higgins, that Hitler had chosen 10th May because this was the date on which the Germans signed the treaty with France after their great victory in 1871. I don't think he knew because he asked if my essay on the Normans was ready.

Dad is thrilled that Chamberlain has gone. He says they called him the Minister of Death when he was Minister of Health back in the Thirties. Dad hates Churchill of course, but thinks he's the right man to deal with Hitler. Just as ruthless, he says. I wouldn't be surprised if we get some bombing soon. If we do, I'll let you know about it, providing I'm not wounded or something equally brave.

Cricket began at school with a real laugh. Loader hit a ball out of the playground (we still can't use the playing fields because of the balloon), straight through the window of a 46 tram which was passing. By the time we'd finished laughing, we realised that the tram hadn't stopped. When we told Haggar, he moaned and groaned about the shortage of cricket balls caused by the war etc., etc., but I believe he was really secretly pleased by one of us making such a big hit. He told us to cycle after the tram and get it back, which had reached New Cross by the time we'd caught up with it. Some daft inspector—the sort who finds out you are travelling without a ticket—grumbled on about the broken window and the fact that several old ladies had been frightened. You can bet that the tram would have to be full of old ladies when the first cricket ball in the history of the world landed inside it. Eventually, after we'd promised that the school would pay and had given Haggar's name, he gave us our ball back.

How does it feel to have the German Army driving in your direction? Come to think of it, if the French fight as badly as usual (look at Waterloo!), you may be shelled before I'm bombed. If you are, make

60

careful notes regardless of danger. They could help me when I write my history of the war.

Saw your dad in the High Street the other day. He seemed to be getting on quite well without you. (Only joking).

Cheerio,
Bill

P.S. Your silver paper pictures sound alright. I expect my aunts would buy them. They are always hanging things from their picture rails. What about sending me some?

P.P.S. And what do I get out of it?

57, St. Mary's Road,
Deal, Kent.
21st June 1940

Dear Bill,

I knew something was up—I just knew it—and I was right! Freddie is selling the house and moving to Oxford. How about that? She's bought a tea shop there and the idea is, that she'll run the shop while Kitty does the cooking. The trouble is, Kitty doesn't want to go and all this week the two of them have done nothing but row with one another. The other night, even after they'd gone to bed, they were still shouting at one another. I heard Freddie yell out at the top of her voice, 'If you want to stay here and be blown to buggery, then you're a stupid little bitch!'. After that, all we could hear was Kitty crying. And by golly Bill, can Kitty cry! I don't know how long she kept up her wailing because I went to sleep, but the next morning at breakfast her eyes were all red and puffy and she was still sniffing and snivelling. Freddie didn't say a word. Just sat there with her mug of tea and chain-smoked and kept muttering 'stupid bitch'. I think they've made it up now because Kitty has stopped crying all over the place.

Anyway, yesterday Freddie told us that they were moving at the end of June. Of course we had to pretend that this was all of a big surprise.

She reckoned that now those rotten Frogs have given in, this bit of the South Coast was really going to be for it. Shells, bombs and maybe gas!!! But don't worry, if I'm not killed, I'll write and tell you all about it.

Ronnie Johnson has told me that he's heard the school is going to move. I asked Mr Morgan and he said he'd never heard such rubbish, so I expect it's true. I'll let you know where we are when we get there.

As you can see, I've been busy on the silver paper pictures. I hope that by now you've got them. When Mum came down last Sunday, she said that she'd get Dad to drop them in at your house. There should have been one more picture, only Mum liked the crinoline lady so much I had to give it to her. This was a pity as I couldn't ask her to pay the full price. I only charged her 1/6, which was almost like giving her a present. So make sure you keep them away from your Mum just in case she want's one as well.

You want to know what YOU are going to get out of it? Well Bill, I've thought about this a lot. How do you feel about 3d a picture? I mean, I've done all the hard work and all you have to do is sell them. After all, 3d a picture is nearly 10% which sounds pretty good to me.

Our class did The Merchant of Venice for the school. It wasn't very good because Gussy Arkwright was rotten as Shylock. Not being big-headed, but I'd have been much better in the part. But Joan Longley did make a point of coming up to me to say how much she liked my Bassanio. Said it was very manly! MANLY!!! How about that? Of course it's possible that she may have noticed that I've now got seven hairs on my chest. But even if she didn't know, I reckon that girls have got a sort of sixth sense about these things.

Your friend,
Merv

7, Nesbit Road,
Eltham, S.E.9.
23rd June 1940

Dear Merv,

Your Freddie's right. They are rotten Frogs. Mum cried when the news came through. I told her we didn't need the bloody French (I didn't say 'bloody' to her, of course); we could beat the Germans on our own. Dad swore a lot and promised that if he had to die he would take at least one German with him. He said he couldn't think of living under Hitler. All this fighting talk only made mum cry even more.

Dad has joined the L.D.V. Don't believe all the newspaper stories about men with pitchforks and broomsticks. Dad has a Canadian Ross rifle which he says is nowhere near as good as a Lee Enfield. Unfortunately he has no ammunition—or rounds as he calls them. Still, we do have his Great War bayonet which we use for chopping firewood. Perhaps it can be put to better use now!!

Do you get an odd feeling when you think of the danger we're all in? There's a sense of waiting. Everybody is glued to the wireless. The weather is marvelous and this somehow makes it worse. The Goodall's, who live two doors up the road, have spoken to us for the first time since we moved in, in 1937. What I didn't realise, is how life just goes on even in a crisis. For example, we had sausages for tea last night, and as I ate them I thought, 'Here I am enjoying sausages and the fate of Britain and the world hangs in the balance'. Made me wonder, how many sausages were eaten before Waterloo? And did the peasants have a good laugh when somebody fell in a muck heap as the Armada came up the Channel? As Bernard Miles would say, 'It makes you think'.

Dad posted my letter to 'Aunt Alice' at Woolwich, so that Mrs Boon wouldn't suspect anything. He thought it was a great laugh, but warned me not to come to him if I got the cane. If only he knew how many times I've had the cane and NOT told him! I signed myself 'Betty Blackford' and complained that I had freckles so none of the boys liked me and what could I do about it? Aunt Alice was brief—quite a change from her lessons. She wrote that a lot of it was in my

63

imagination and boys probably did like me but I hadn't noticed—so, just buck up Betty Blackford! What a daft reply. Typical of a woman in love with Haggar.

I told some of the girls and they brought their copies of this female trash to school. No boy dare do it because Mrs Boon might have smelt a rat. I think she's beginning to wonder why her readers have trebled to nine! Apparently she has signed on for Fire Watch at the school— with Haggar, of course! She looks a real Greta Garbo with her tin hat on.

My Uncle Fred made me laugh a few days ago. His brother, who has become a Christadelphian, says he won't die; he will just be 'called'— and presumably disappear. Actually, he's no fool. The army has left him out because of his beliefs, so really he hasn't been 'called'. Uncle Fred said that it was very funny that his religious conversion should happen just as the war broke out!!!

Cheerio,
Bill

P.S.   Your dad's just come round with your silver paper pictures. I've only had a quick look as mum's around, but they don't look too bad.

'My Uncle Fred made me laugh...' Bill's Uncle Fred was a shoemaker

57, St. Mary's Road,
Deal. Kent.
25th June 1940

Dear Bill,

Suddenly all sorts of things are happening down here! The school is moving tomorrow but no one's told us where we're going yet. Johnny Jackson said it's the same with his Dad in the army. It's all to do with National Security. Anyway, when we get to wherever it is we're going, I'll let you know.

Now here's some REAL WAR NEWS!!! Everyone down here is saying that the Germans tried to invade us the other day. Some think it was on the 23rd, but others reckon it was on the 21st. It was during the night at St. Margaret's Bay, which isn't far from here. They must have been pretty quiet about it because Walter and I didn't hear a thing, and neither did Ronnie Johnson or anyone else at school. I knew you'd want to know all about it so I spoke to this boatman. He's on the lifeboat as well and he sometimes stops to talk to me. He's very brave. He took his small boat over to Dunkirk and brought back twenty soldiers. He would have made a second trip only his engine packed up. He said it was like sailing into Hell and back. He got very angry about how our men had suffered and said it should never have happened. He reckons that it's because we have such bad generals and Churchill should sack the lot of them.

Anyway, he knew all about this German invasion and said it was perfectly true. According to him, the Germans had tried to land in small barges that they'd towed over. But we'd been expecting this and had been very clever. We had sunk some oil or petrol drums in the sea in places where we thought they might land. There were two lots of them. Once the Germans got in close, we set fire to the ones in the sea behind them. Then we set fire to the sea in front of them so that they were trapped in the middle. Every one of them was burnt to a cinder!!! He said they are still finding bodies washed up on the beach. It was a great victory, only he couldn't understand why we were keeping so quiet about it. There's been nothing in the papers.

Afterwards, Ronnie and I went for a long walk along the beach hoping to find some of these German bodies. All we found was an unexploded mine with a soldier guarding it who told us to bugger off. Still, I do think it's worth writing about in your war diary.

I'll be sorry to leave Freddie and Kitty but I'm going to make damned sure I don't get stuck with Walter again. He's a pain in the neck. You know how much pocket money he gets each week—well, I asked him to lend me a bob for a smashing idea I have to make some money. Only I need it for tomorrow, because that's the only day it will work. He said no. So, I even offered to pay him back 1/6 for just a twentyfour hour loan. All he could say, was that the teachers wouldn't like it. Stupid sod. Then Freddie asked me what was wrong and I told her. She laughed and gave me a shilling, so now I'm going to do it on my own. I've just seen the clock. I've got to get to the bakers before they close and then I have to pack. Will write to you when I get there.

Your friend,
Merv

Nowhere.
26th June 1940

Dear Bill,

I can't give you my address because I don't know where I am. I think it's at a place called Rude Herring—at least that's what it sounded like. Anyway, I do know we're in Wales and it's not far from Newport, Monmouthshire.

I'm writing this by the light of a candle in a school hall in this place called Rude Herring. There's five of us. After they fed us, they put mattresses on the floor and now they've gone off and left us for the night, so I thought I'd write it all down while I can remember it. Anyway, there's nothing else to do. So, I'll start at the beginning.

We left Deal about nine. Kitty and Freddie came to the station, but of course Kitty had to cry all over the place, didn't she? Freddie tried to shut her up only she just kept on crying and saying how she

66

wouldn't see us again and that Freddie never did have any feelings or she'd be crying as well—which made Freddie really blow her lid. Thank God the train started on time. The last I saw of Freddie and Kitty was the pair of them shouting at one another. I don't think they noticed us going because they were still arguing when the train pulled out. They never even bothered to wave.

Ronnie Johnson, Johnny Jackson and I were in the same carriage and as soon as Walter went for a tinkle—as my sister always says—we agreed that we'd try to get billeted together—and certainly without Walter. The journey went on and on, just like the first time, stopping, starting and going backwards. We were stuck in the sidings, at Reading I think it was, for nearly an hour. I'd planned on it being a long journey and I was right. Yesterday I'd gone to the bakers and for a shilling I bought 24 stale buns. When I told him the school was leaving Deal for an unknown destination and I was buying the buns for my mates because no one was going to feed us, the baker gave me another two dozen for free. Kitty had to give me a shopping bag to put them all in. Everyone had finished their milk and sandwiches by one o'clock but I waited and waited and come four o'clock the whole train was starving. So, that's when I went up and down the corridor with the buns. I sold the lot at 2d each and wished I'd bought more. I saved one for myself and when I got back to the carriage Walter wanted to buy it, but I said no. He really is a guts because he offered me 6d for it, but I told him he'd had his chance yesterday. Then I ate it in front of him— very slowly. It tasted awful but it was smashing just to watch him squirm. He got so angry he went bright red and stumped off out of the carriage. Ten minutes after that we arrived at Newport, so I only got rid of them just in time.

Then it was into the charabancs. Some of the school went to Bassaleg and we came on to this Rude Herring place. It was raining when we got here but they still herded us together in the playground in front of all these foster parents. Bloody Hell, Bill, it was awful!!! The women kept on nipping into the crowd of us and dragging one or two out. There was even a farmer who came around some of the bigger boys and was feeling their muscles, until the bloke in charge went up

67

to him and said, 'Fair do, Mr Williams, this isn't a cattle market.' Well, you could have fooled me, because that's just what it did feel like. D'you know who the farmer took in the end? Walter! Fat lot of work he'll get out of him.

Finally, all the foster parents went and there were still five of us left. Ronnie Johnson, Johnny Jackson, Bob Thorne, Charles Burton and me. By now it was six o'clock and the bloke in charge was looking very worried. Then three of his helpers went and he disappeared into the school. He just left us standing out in the playground in all that bloody rain. Johnny said, 'Bugger this for a lark, I'm going to hitch a ride back to London.' But just then, this bloke came out of the school beaming all over his face and told us that we were 'very privileged boys'—only we'd have to wait until tomorrow. Then some women turned up with blankets, mattresses and others brought soup and sandwiches. If I don't blow the candle out the others say they'll scrag me.

Merv

Machen House,
Lower Machen,
Monmouthshire.
28th June 1940

Dear Bill,

How about this for an address?!! By golly, you wait until I tell you what it's like. After breakfast this big car arrives at the school and this lady, Mrs Griffiths, says to the bloke in charge, 'How many have you got, Mr Thomas?' 'Five ma'am', he says. 'Oh, I think I can just about manage five.' And with that we were all taken out to the car, where the driver strapped our cases on to the back. We all got in and there was plenty of room because there were two spare seats that folded up from the floor. Mrs Griffiths sat in the front with the driver only we couldn't talk to them because there was a glass window that shut them off.

Machen House, Lower Machen

Then we were off. Of course we didn't know where we were going—could have been to Timbuctoo for all we knew. After a while we turned off the main road and came to the gates of this big house. As we drove up the drive we were all speechless—all, except Johnny who kept muttering, 'Bloody Hell, Bloody Hell.' Bill, the front lawn is so big, you could easily get two football pitches into it and still have room to spare!!! And there's a tennis court and two lakes with a rowing boat and a pigsty and lots of garages and buildings and a stream and a fish pond. And the rest of the garden is huge—bigger than both our roads put together!!!!

It's all surrounded by a high brick wall so that no one can see in. We even have a private gate to the church next door—not that we'll be going there. Oh yes, here's something historical for you. The church was built in 940—so it's exactly a thousand years old.

We all sleep in a big room at the back of the house in the servants quarters. At least four of us do. Charles is sleeping in a house nearby with Mrs Griffiths mother—Lady Walker! How about that for a bit of swank?

69

Downstairs there's a green baize door that shuts us off from the rest of the house, so I don't know what that bit is like yet. There's two servants that live in the house, Mrs Evans, she's the cook, and Jenny the maid. Mrs Evans is nice and round and fat and she must be at least fifty. Jenny is a real good looker, tall and dark with a smashing figure—but has she got a sharp tongue! The man who drives the car is called Albert. He's thin and quite old. He lives over the garages and looks after the gardens. He doesn't talk much and I don't think he likes us.

The others are all playing outside in the garden—or as us posh people say—in the grounds. Let me know how you're getting on selling those pictures of mine and write soon.

Your friend,
Merv

Albert the gardener, all poshed up for a wedding

70

Machen House,
Lower Machen,
Monmouthshire.
23rd July 1940

Dear Bill,

I've been waiting nearly a month for your reply and I'm worried that I haven't heard from you for such a long time. We've heard all about your air raids and bombing, so that's why I'm wondering if you're all right. What's it like in Eltham? Has your house been blown up or have you had any bombs near you? I've had two letters from Mum saying that everything is fine and that I mustn't worry about them—which only makes me worry. I do wish everyone would stop treating me as though I were still a kid.

We're off school now until the middle of September, which is smashing. We've hardly been out of the grounds as there's so much to do inside. We were practicing diving in the big lake the other day. After several belly-flops, I did a really deep one—just like Tarzan diving off a cliff—only I got my head stuck in the mud at the bottom. By golly Bill, was I scared! It seemed ages before I could pull myself free. When I did finally come up for air, all the others fell about laughing because my head was completely covered in black mud—just two frightened eyes peering out!! With all this hot weather we spend practically the whole day in our bathing trunks, so we're all very brown.

We've been given the use of one of the outhouses for a playroom. There's a ping-pong table, dart board and a gramophone. We've only got three records though—'A tisket a tasket', 'Boom' and 'Music maestro please', and we know the words of all of them. Above the playroom there's a tower where they used to store apples and you can get out on to the roof where you can see for miles. We have great swordfights up and down the stairs.

The two Griffiths girls are home from school. One's called Heather and the other, Rosemary. They're not bad looking. (I think Ronnie's fallen for Heather.) For girls, they are all right and join in with most of the things we get up to.

71

Oh yes, I haven't told you about Captain Griffiths yet, have I? Rosemary says he was in the Great War and did lots of brave things and has medals to prove it. He works away from home all week but comes back at the week-end. He's not very big but never stops charging around the place doing things. He's got a very posh voice and finishes every sentence with 'what?' And not just one 'what'—sometimes several. Such as, 'What d'you think, what? What-what-what!' Just like a machine gun. It's never always the same though. It might be, 'Eh, what-what-what?' Or 'What, what, eh?' Or 'What? Eh? What, what?' Or even, 'Doncha know? What? Eh?' When he's not around, Ronnie, Johnny and I are what-whatting all over the place.

First thing he does on a Saturday morning is to get the big mowing machine out. Our job is to empty the grass clippings. He's got a spare box and Ronnie and I station ourselves at either end of the lawn. Two or three times up and down and the box is full. Then it's on with the spare box and off he goes again. It takes 2 hours to do that lawn and he never stops once. By then, we're completely shagged, but he charges off to do something else. But he does give us sixpence each. Old Albert dodges around the place trying to keep out of his way, but sometimes the Captain catches up with him in the potting shed or pigsty and then Albert gets gunned down by a blast of what-whatting.

We got it in the neck last week though. On Friday night we decided to dam the stream that runs through the grounds. It was a smashing dam and we'd built it really high and packed it with mud. The first sign we had of trouble was on the Saturday afternoon when Mrs Evans stumped out to see the Captain. She was in a right old state and we heard her say, 'Well, if you want any dinner today, you'd better find out what's wrong'. When the Captain discovered our dam he really blew his lid! In five seconds flat, he'd torn it to pieces. Later on, when he'd calmed down, he explained that the stream supplied all the water for the house. 'Just don't do anything like that again, lads—what-eh-what-whatwhat!?' I think that secretly he was quite impressed by our dam. I'm not drinking anymore water because Johnny often pees in that stream. He pees in the lake as well. He'll pee anywhere.

We haven't had any air raids here yet. I suppose it's because there's nothing worth bombing. But we have seen searchlights over Newport and Cardiff and heard guns in the distance.

Do try to sell my silver-paper pictures, Bill. Mum's said she's going to send my bike down but I know it needs new brakes, so I can do with some extra money. And providing you're not dead, I expect a letter by return of post.

Your friend,
Merv

Machen House,
Lower Machen,
Monmouthshire,
10th August 1940

Dear Bill,

This is your last chance!!!! It's no good pretending that you're dead or wounded because I know you're not. I was very worried about you so I wrote to Mum. Only the day before she got my letter, my Mum and Dad had met your Mum and Dad coming out of the Well Hall Odeon and they asked after you. They were told that you were 'fighting fit'. Those were the exact words your Dad used. So don't come up with the excuse that you've had a sprained wrist—because I know all!! I mean, it was your idea that we should write to one another, not mine. While I'm busy writing to you, the others are always outside having a fine old time. I've got plenty of other things to do, so if you want to stop, just say so. I'll write to someone else instead, I don't care. This could be the very last letter you get from me. But I hope it isn't. It's up to you, Bill.

We've now got another member of our gang. His name is Gavin Young and he's a cousin of the Griffiths girls. He's come to stay with them over the school holidays—or hols as he calls them. He's a complete madcap, a real daredevil. At first we weren't sure if we'd like him because when Heather told us he was coming, she said that he was a real tough nut and if it came to a fight he would easily beat any one of us—probably all of us put together. Then Rosemary said that he went to a school where they had a cold shower every morning before breakfast and then they went out and played rugby and as his father was a General, he was used to fighting, it was in his blood. This didn't sound good at all. I mean, as you know, I don't mind a scrap, but I didn't like the idea of having to belt him one as soon as he arrived. Hardly seemed friendly. Charles, who's a nice chap but never says a great deal, quietly put in his twopennyworth and suggested that instead of making up our minds now, we wait to see what he was like. And as it turned out, this was good advice. Clever bugger, Charles.

When he turned up, the first thing Gavin suggested was that we have a battle. Two teams. One to defend the tower and the other to try to capture it. I had Johnny and Bob on my side, defending, and Gavin had Ronnie and Charles attacking. They got on to the roof of the tower and Gavin found an old iron bar and started to smash the windows in. Luckily Bob—and this was a brave thing to do—grabbed the bar and held on. He nearly pulled Gavin over the roof—and that would have been the end of a very short friendship. After we got the bar, they attacked up the stairs with wooden staves but we had a good supply of rotten apples and managed to beat them off. It was a tremendous battle and lasted most of the morning. In the end we called it a draw. Just as well, otherwise we'd have completely wrecked the place.

After lunch—oh yes, we don't call it dinner now, but lunch, even though it's the same meal as dinner—then we have tea and supper. Dinner is like lunch only you have it at night and then you miss out supper. This way you can have two dinners in one day. At home, on a Sunday, we have High Tea. And we always have it in the front room—even if we haven't got visitors. We start with peaches or pears with Libby's milk, and then we have ham or salmon or pilchards with salad. After that, it's one of Mum's Victoria sponges or some of her buns. Then, when everyone goes into the kitchen to wash up, I stay in the front room with the lights out and watch the fire. In the winter when the muffin man comes round, we toast crumpets by the fire. When I was small, Dad used to take me up to Blackheath pond to sail my boat. It was made by Uncle Bertie and called Bluebell. This was a model of the ship in which he sailed around the world. To walk back home through an autumn fog and then have crumpets by the fire was bloody marvelous. Funny I should think about that now when it's blazing hot outside.

Sorry, I got a bit lost. Yes, I was telling you about that first day with Gavin. In the afternoon he showed us a smashing trick. We lit a fire in the playroom, then collected up a load of empty lemonade bottles. What you do, is put just a bit of water in and screw them down tight. Then you put one on the fire, run like hell to the other end of the room and take cover behind a table. You get a fantastic explosion. Glass showers everywhere. It's super!!

That night, Mrs Evans allowed us to take our cocoa across to the playroom before bed. Only because it was Gavin who asked her. One of us and she'd have said no. So, we got the fire going again and just sat around and talked. That's when it all came out. Gavin told us that Heather and Rosemary had got him properly rattled. They said that we were real tough guys from the East End of London and that all the local boys were scared stiff of us. (I don't know how, because we haven't met any yet.) They told him that the best thing he could do, was to pick a fight with one of us to prove that he was as tough as we were. Now, it would have to be a girl to think up a rotten trick like that, wouldn't it? And that's the reason we kept on seeing them lurking behind bushes and peering at us all day. We made a solemn vow to get our own back on them. Then we marked Gavin's forehead with hot charcoal from the fire to show that he was one of us now.

Mum and Vevlie came down last week-end. We went into Newport. They bought me a raincoat and we all had our photo taken together at Jerome's. Then we went back to the house where we had tea with Mrs Griffiths in the drawing room. It's the first time I've seen what it's like on the other side of the green baize door. It's very grand, Bill. There's a winding staircase, real marble tiles in the hall, which is as big as our kitchen and front room put together. We had lots of little cucumber sandwiches. Trouble was, one mouthful and they were all gone.

Afterwards, I took Mum and Vev up to the station-master's house where they were staying. The next morning Mum said she hadn't slept a wink all night because it was so quiet. I couldn't understand this until Vev took me on one side to explain. It's the noise of the air raids in London and sleeping in the shelter every night that was the cause of the trouble. She said that everyone had now grown quite used to it, and then to sleep in a feather bed and suddenly have all that quiet around, was a bit worrying. I thought I understood what she was getting at but now I'm not sure. Mum enjoyed the visit and kept on saying how much I'd grown and how brown I was. Then she got a bit weepy until Vev said, 'Now then, Mum, pull yourself together, don't be such a fool.' Vev can be a bit bossy at times.

Dad has been offered a job up in North Wales and so has Vev. Dad's is as a foreman in a munitions factory and Vev is going to be one of Lord Woolton's secretaries. They are going to move up there soon I think. I suppose Eric will stay on at Kenward Road. I hope I don't have to go up to North Wales, although it would be good to be with Mum and Dad again. But as Mum says, it may not happen.

Don't forget. Write soon!!!

Your friend,

Merv

Mervyn, with his mother and sister immediately after buying 'the raincoat' in Newport

7, Nesbit Road,
Eltham, S.E.9.
26th August 1940

Dear Merv,

There's no need to get on your high horse. It may be all right for you living in your big country house, even though you are doing your best to smash it up, but we peasants have to dig gardens and spend time trying to sell other peoples silver-paper pictures and do all sorts of jobs for ourselves because we haven't got servants to wait on us. No, seriously Merv, it sounds as though you've really landed on your feet and right now, I wish I were down there with you and this Gavin, who sounds like one of us. And I'm very sorry not to have written before but so much has been happening!

Our first air raid warning was at 1am on 25th June—there's historical accuracy for you. The first raid itself was Sunday 18th August, when I saw two enemy planes. They were silvery and seemed to be doing a dance in the sky. Perhaps they were fighting our planes. I don't know. On 23rd June I saw my first enemy plane close up. It was a wrecked Heinkel 111 being towed on a trailer along the Rochester Way. I bet they wouldn't tow one of our wrecked planes about in broad daylight!! Aeroplanes look very tinny when you see them close up. Very frail looking—especially after they've crashed.

Soon afterwards, the nights became exciting. We spend a great deal of time in our Anderson shelter in the garden. I expect your mum and dad are doing the same in Kenward Road. We share our shelter with the Collins, who haven't got one. The game is to see whether the searchlights can catch a plane and the guns on Woolwich common shoot it down. The searchlight part seems easy; the guns are hopeless. We really got excited when the first one was spotlighted. First one beam, then two, three and four searchlights all swung across the sky and caught it. It was really thrilling! We could see the German markings quite clearly. Every minute we expected it to be shot down because the noise of gunfire was deafening. No such luck! It just droned on and on without a scratch, whilst showers of shrapnel clattered down in the road. I'm making a collection. You have to wait

77

until it cools down of course, until you can pick it up. Dad swore a lot. He hates all aircraft because he was machine-gunned by Richtofen's red 'circus' in the Great War. He's always said that he'll never travel in one, though I can't see how he could afford it anyway.

Our Anderson is quite cosy. We have laid old carpets on the floor and this keeps out the damp, at least while the weather stays dry. We have plenty of pillows and blankets for sleeping and benches set around the walls, which are concreted up to ground level. The top of this concrete forms a ledge on which we store valuables—a bottle of water (stale), a flat candle like a night-light with a cardboard guard to stop it being blown out, and of course, our gasmasks, snug in their cases—dad bought me a leather one for Christmas. We also have several old broom sticks to push away firebombs. Once we are all in, dad closes up the entrance with an old blackboard we got from the school across the road.

As soon as the siren goes—which is usually about eight o'clock at night—we all troop out to the shelter. The females bring loads of rubbish in handbags; Mrs Collins always has some knitting 'on the go', as she puts it. She knits much faster when a plane is overhead! Dad brings a small attaché case with his insurance policies in it. If we're bombed, his plan is to send the claim straight to Hitler, addressed to whatever shelter the bastard is hiding in! Dad says we've all become troglodytes—no don't bother looking it up, you country bumkin, I'll tell you—cave-dwellers. It's a good word, isn't it? He says that it reminds him of the trenches. A few nights ago, I asked him whether he carried his insurance policies with him in the Great War. He laughed and said that all he had was a small copy of the New Testament, issued to all soldiers, and in the back there was a section where you could make your Will. Very cheering that was, he said. He somehow lost the letter from Lord Kitchener which advised the troops to remain pure, treat women with respect and stay away from them. Difficult to do both, but it sounds just like the stupid sort of thing Haggar would say.

Mrs Collins is alright—there's no problem in treating her with respect. Her two daughters are ghastly; the real problem is to stay away from them because it's not exactly private sitting in the shelter all night, knees almost touching. The women get embarrassed if they have to go indoors to the lavatory and make up all sorts of excuses like, 'I think I'll have a glass of water'. We men are quite happy to pee in the garden. We keep away from the vegetables, so it's the flowers that get it. Of course, you can only nip out during a lull in the bombing. The youngest Collins, a witch called Sheila, always seems to be in her house when a bomber roars over really low or the barrage starts up again. She rushes back looking very uncomfortable and it's obvious she's either not started or not finished what she went to do. You don't know her. She goes to some posh private school in Blackheath, so it's fun to think of her sitting on the bog with her knickers down shivering with fear. When she gets back, I give her one of my slow, sardonic, knowing smiles—just like Basil Rathbone does—so she knows exactly what I'm thinking. She goes bright red, and if her mother's not looking, pokes her tongue out.

The school holidays are nearly over. What sort of term we shall have if the bombing continues to go on at this rate I don't know. The daily score of enemy planes shot down makes good headlines, but dad says the best thing to do is divide them by half and take away the first number you thought of. Still, I think the RAF is winning the Battle of Britain, as everyone calls it. I hope we are, only we didn't do too well against the Romans and Normans did we?

As for you, didn't I tell you that the Germans were after you? If the Channel hadn't been in the way you could have done something really brave, like killing ten thousand Germans with your bare hands! Oh yes, you know the Blackfen Road near Avery Hill Park, well they've built some concrete pill-boxes and they are manned by the Home Guard. Perhaps the Germans will run away at the sight of them. Bet you didn't know this, but it was the Germans who invented pill-boxes at Ypres in the Great War. I know history doesn't interest you like it does me, that's why your letters never contain any fascinating bits about pill-boxes in them.

All the signposts were taken away long ago but now they are covering up place-names as well. The Post Office bloke at Eltham Park has fixed a piece of wood over the name 'Eltham'. That should really worry a German tank commander!! Actually, it might work. A lot of people really are getting lost. But if they ask you where they are, you're not supposed to tell them just in case they're spies or fifth columnists.

Are you being told to collect salvage? We are. Paper, bones, cardboard, waste rags, metal, pots and pans—all for the war effort. The railings by the church, the ones poor old Jean Taylor got stuck on that night, they've been taken away to build guns, tanks, planes or something warlike. I bet Jean wishes they'd been taken away before she sat on those spikes; I can hear her screams now. When we get back to school perhaps I'll mention it to her, though it's a bit unkind considering she was in hospital for a month.

Talking of salvage, why don't you hand in some of your old essays (waste paper) or your bike (tin) for the war effort. And talking of essays, you never use a semi-colon, it's always a hyphen. Miss Wilcox says it's a sign of sloppy writing. Just thought I'd mention it. Damn, there goes the siren yet again. I've written this letter between going back and forth to the shelter six times today. They are getting nearer and I think this is going to be a big one, so will close now.

Cheerio,
Bill

Machen House,
Lower Machen,
Monmouthshire,
29th August 1940

Dear Bill,

Sod your Miss Wilcox. If I want to use a — I'll use a — and not a ;. Hyphens are modern. You're so filled up with history that you're stuck in the past surrounded by hordes of old fashioned semi-colons.

By golly, from the sound of it, you're really going through it. But you don't give any details. I mean, how many houses have been blown up and how many people have been killed? It makes me feel very out of it down here but if the Germans land they'll find us prepared for them. We've now got our own army.

This is how it happened. A couple of weeks ago, Colonel Griffiths— oh yes, he's now a Colonel in the Home Guard—came home, lined us all up on the lawn and said we were going to have a serious talk, man to man. This country now had its back to the wall and the Germans could invade at any moment. They would probably come by sea but they could also drop on us from out of the sky. We should keep a particular look-out for parachutists and if we met anyone who had a strange accent, then one of us should tail him while the other went for the police. I felt like saying that everyone around here had a strange accent but I thought it best to keep quiet.

We boys were the men of the house and above all we should make sure that the women came to no harm while he was away. Then he said, dismiss and marched off. We were all quiet for a bit after that. I don't know about the others, but I suddenly felt quite grown up. I suppose it was because he treated us like men and not boys. Anyway, this got us talking about how to defend Machen House against the Nazis. We knew how to cut the water off, but that wouldn't kill them and they probably didn't wash anyway. We started off with catapults. We found an inner tube and old Albert let us cut it up into strips. They're really powerful. Then we had some real luck. In one of the outhouses we found a stack of lemonade bottles with marbles in them, so now we each have a pouch with twenty rounds of ammunition. The trouble is, you can't kill anyone with a marble—and don't tell me about David and Goliath because my bet is, he used a bloody great rock.

Anyway, Charles, who thinks and reads a lot, came up with the idea of the long bow, reminding us of how they won the day at Agincourt. We decided on yew because it's got a lot of spring and the churchyard next door was full of it. Luckily we have a lot of bamboo growing in the grounds, so they made the arrows. We tried to catch a duck to give us the feathers for the flights but whenever we got near, the buggers flew off. Our arrows don't have flights at all. That window in the tower that Gavin smashed in was full of lead panes, so we used the lead to wrap around the end of the arrow. By golly Bill, they go for miles. If you're thinking of making one, use waxed string. Ordinary string breaks.

We spend a lot of time practising. What we do, is mark out an area on the ground, then the six of us stand about a hundred yards away and try to get our arrows into that area. After we've fired, we run for cover and take up a new position to aim from. We've each got four arrows, so I reckon that as the Nazis march up the drive, by the time they've reached the house, we could have killed at least twenty of them. The arrows are really deadly because after we've sharpened them, we put them in the fire to harden.

Last week-end we thought we were really for it. The Colonel was showing Gavin's father around—he's not a General but just a Brigadier—when the vicar from next door came charging up to complain that not only had we trampled over holy ground but that we'd torn all the branches off his yew trees. Unfortunately, at that moment Ronnie, Johnny and I appeared carrying our bows. Up stamped the Colonel and the other two. The vicar grabbed Ronnie's bow and started babbling on about 'evidence' and being 'caught red handed', but the Colonel soon shut him up and demanded an explanation. Of course, when we told him that the only reason we'd got them was to defend the house and kill Germans, he was a pleased as Punch and said to the vicar that he should look on it as the church's war effort.

When we pointed out our ambush positions, the Colonel and the Brigadier went into a long discussion about 'fields of fire' and got quite excited about the whole idea. When the Colonel asked about the range, I said I'd show him, and shot one off up into the air. I hadn't noticed that Bob Thorne was stretched out sunbathing on the tennis court. My arrow was heading straight for him!!! We all looked on in horror until I finally yelled out. And as Bob rolled over to see who was calling, the arrow thudded into the grass right beside him. It went into the ground a good foot!!! I think the Colonel and the Brigadier were most impressed. Bob wasn't. After they'd gone he gave me a really good boot up the backside. I can't say I blame him.

Of course, we're not in the thick of it like you, all we hear is distant gunfire, but if they do invade, we'll be ready for them.

Your friend,
Merv

7, Nesbit Road,
Eltham, S.E.9.
15th September 1940

Dear Merv,

I don't know how much you've heard down in your backwater but here's the story as it happened on the night of 7-8th September. Surely it will become an historic date?

Mum was just making tea early Saturday evening after a shopping expedition to Beresford Square. The siren sounded and as usual we went out to the shelter. Mum went down but dad and I stayed up top keeping a look-out. It was a lovely warm evening. Soon the roar of aeroplane engines was heard. As you know, we've been seeing a lot of enemy planes lately but this time we somehow sensed it was different. In spite of all the noise, there was a feeling of stillness, and believe it or not, a dog howled. Dad said this was a bad sign. Sure enough, when the bombers appeared there were too many to count. They flew in massed formation like we saw in the newsreels of the Spanish Civil War. Although we've had a lot of raids it was the first time I really felt the war in my guts. I felt angry too. How dare they fly over my country as though they owned it. Who the hell do these scum think they are? Just then, some puffs of smoke, though no sound, showed that the shells were bursting around them.

'Get the buggers!' I shouted and just then I saw my first plane hit. It spiralled away and came down with black smoke pouring from its tail. We jumped with joy. 'Hope they're dead or still burning', yelled dad.

as the guns crash, and bombs
fall When they do. look out the
whole sky is one mass of
eddying black smoke. At last ;
the all clear goes and John and
his mother and father crawl from
the shelter. The fire - engines
stationed across the road at the
school are tearing out. John
jumps on his bike and rides
furiously after them. He cannot
keep up with them, now and then
and by this he is able to
follow them. His route is along
the Rochester Way cut off
into Kidbrooke Park road,
he chars along past the "Roxy" (cinema)
round the round-about and on
to the top of Westcombe Hill
12

Part of Bill's original account for 8th September 1940.
He wrote in the third person, calling himself 'John'

Bill with the bicycle on which he had 'a wild ride' 7th September 1940

In between these kind thoughts, he'd worked out that the bombers were heading for Silvertown and the Arsenal. If that was the target then we were quite safe. Soon we could hear the scream of falling bombs and then the explosions began. Two, three, six, eight and more and more. After a time I stopped counting the crashes. There was no need to guess at the damage because the sky was filling up with so much smoke that it blotted out the evening sun. Already, fire engines were clanging their way out of the school gate opposite. (The AFS is based there.) Mum didn't want me to go but dad said I'd be safe enough, so I jumped on my bike and tried to keep up with the fire engines. It was a wild ride and I'll never forget it. Up Rochester Way, down Kidbrooke Park Road, past the Roxy to the roundabout at the top of Westcombe Hill. There was no need to go any further. Bloody hell Merv, I only wish I could describe to you what I saw, because spread out before me was the sort of sight Pepys must have seen during the Great Fire of London.

The north side of the river was a mass of flames. Tall factory buildings like Tate and Lyle, Henleys and Siemens, poked their heads out of the smoke. Flames were licking from their square windows,

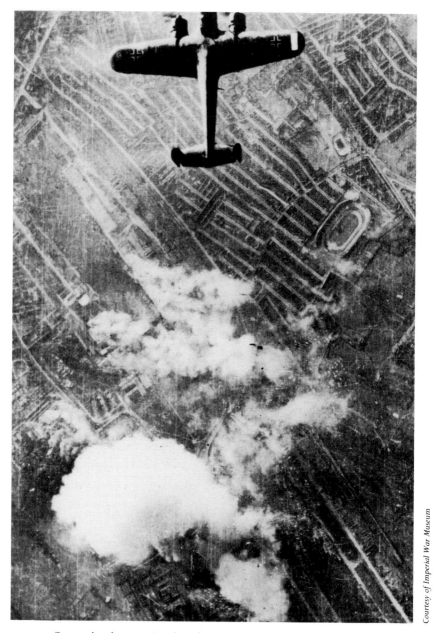

German bomber over Royal Docks, East London, 7th September 1940.
The sky above Woolwich is blotted out by smoke

Courtesy of Imperial War Museum

making them look like burning crosswords! As it started to get dark, the sky began to to take on the fierce glow of the furnace that was burning below. Even the Thames, which I've since found out was full of burning gin, rum, brandy and sugar from the warehouses, seemed to be on fire, which of course it was. My first thoughts were historical—you know me! Napoleon's sight of Moscow burning; that sort of thing. Then I thought of the human beings in the middle of all that. I already know what a wrecked building can do to a person, crushing limbs and squashing innards! This time people were burning. We've always looked down on the North Woolwich scruffs, haven't we? Well, now those poor old scruffs were burning.

I felt cold and suddenly noticed that I was almost alone. The few spectators that were there when I arrived had all drifted off to their homes or public shelters. As I slowly rode home, a second wave of bombers droned overhead, making straight for the fire, and more fire engines raced by with their bells clanging. That night I read a book in the garden by the glow of all those fires, even though they were about five miles away. And all the time we could hear the bombers droning overhead. They never seemed to stop. God knows how many there were. It was 6 a.m. on Sunday before the All Clear sounded and we went indoors to bed.

When I got up at mid-day I was surprised to see a large double-decker bus outside, almost blocking the road. It's not something you expect to see in Nesbit Road with its four terraced houses and only two hundred yards from end to end. Clambering out of the bus were refugees, the sort we've only seen on newsreels. It was a sight I never thought I'd see in this country!! They were the homeless from North Woolwich. Some had battered old cases, some had bundles of clothing and other belongings. A few seemed cheerful but most of them were silent, sad or crying. But they all had a dazed, dusty look which I shall never forget. They were coming to the school which had been opened as an Emergency Rest Centre. Rest Centre? They must have thought that name up before the war. All of them were starving hungry, so mum and Mrs Collins made them tea and took over biscuits as well and any other food they could rake up.

87

Later, dad and I had a talk with the bus driver. He told a stirring tale. Every factory from North Woolwich to Southend had been flattened, he claimed. God knows how he could be so sure about Southend. As for houses, the whole lot had gone.

The next day, dad and I cycled to Woolwich and took the ferry. I suppose it was more of a shock to dad than me, because he used to work at Siemens and knows the area better than I do. There was just street after street of empty, ruined houses with gutted factories stuck in the middle. Near Henleys, the cable makers, the melted rubber had gone solid in large pools all over the road. Dad said it is called gutter-percha and when I jumped up and down on it, it was just like a spring board. Felt very strange.

The night after the big raid, there were more attacks. The searchlights made so many criss-cross patterns that dad got his Brownie out and took eight pictures. The chemist looked a bit surprised when he handed them over today. No wonder. They were all blank.

Courtesy of Hulton-Deutsch

'The searchlights made so many criss-cross patterns'

There's been some local bombing since then. We are all right but there's plaster all over the floors and the front and back door locks are wrecked. The house took such a shaking from the blast that dirt has come out of all the nooks and crannies that mum never even knew was there. She's quite ashamed. Well, you know what a clean and tidy person she is! We told her it's better to have a dirty house rather than no house at all, but she still keeps going on about it. In the end, I suggested she asked all the neighbours in to inspect the dirt for themselves, but she didn't laugh, just told me not to be so cheeky. Actually I shouldn't make fun of her because she has a weak heart and is often frightened both for herself and us. She also got very upset because two days ago we came in from the shelter to find our canary was dead. It may have been fright or blast. We don't know. Obadiah, our cat has disappeared again, but then he did that before the war. In any case, he's about as patriotic as my uncle's brother, the Christadelphian I told you about. Write soon.

Cheerio,
Bill

P.S.   Your silver paper pictures are quite safe. But this is not really the time to go around trying to sell them.

Machen House,
Lower Machen,
Monmouthshire.
18th September 1940

Dear Bill,

Your letter arrived this morning. I read it out to the others after breakfast. Even Mrs Evans came in from the kitchen to listen. She has a brother who works on the railways at Paddington. She said it was a very dramatic letter and beautifully written. Mrs Evans goes to chapel a lot. She said she wasn't too happy about the swearing in your letter, but as it was to do with Germans, then probably God would forgive the bad language. The others were most impressed. After breakfast we all sat down and wrote home to make sure that everyone was all right.

Don't laugh but I now sing in the choir every Sunday. Twice. All of us do. And don't go thinking we've suddenly got religious, because we haven't. It was all the fault of the vicar. He came to see Mrs Griffiths one day when we were having a sing-song out in the playroom. Unfortunately he heard us. I have the feeling that it was bloody 'Danny Boy' that did it. Anyway, beaming all over his face, he said that such beautiful voices should be heard by all and would we like to sing in the choir? This was met by a deathly silence. Then he said, 'Perhaps I should add that each boy is paid sixpence.' So we quickly said yes and Charles muttered something about thirty pieces of silver.

Jenny, the maid, has been causing a bit of trouble lately. She didn't like the idea of us having a lie-in every morning. I mean, after all, we are on holiday. Each day it was the same. Half past seven, she'd yell up the stairs for us to get up. At a quarter to eight, she'd march in and go round throwing the bedclothes off each of us. We got really fed up with this. So one night I went to bed without my pyjama trousers on. Next morning when she called up the stairs, I didn't go back to sleep as usual, but stayed awake. I lay there for the next fifteen minutes thinking about what Jenny would look like with all her clothes off. So when she came to pull back my bedclothes, she really got an eyeful I can tell you!!! She just stood there staring, then she gave a scream and ran out of the room. Since then, she only stands in the doorway.

All this thinking about Jenny in the nude made me wonder what she'd really be like, because although she's got a sharp tongue, she's also got a smashing figure and long dark hair—a bit like Hedy Lamarr. Wow!!! Have I got a story to tell you, Bill!!? We have our bath on Friday night and Jenny always has hers on a Thursday afternoon. Well, I discussed the problem with the others. Ronnie, who plans to be an engineer like Brunel, came up with a really good idea. There's a trapdoor in the bathroom ceiling which is always left half open to let the steam out. By rigging up three mirrors, you could sit well back in the loft and see all of the bathroom.

It worked a treat. The only trouble was, if you were discovered, you couldn't escape. Also, someone lying back in the bath might wonder what a mirror was doing up in the loft. The answer was so simple. The bathroom has two windows and one of these is over the back stairs. This has coloured paper stuck on it to look like stained glass. I scraped away a small bit of paper, then went outside to the back stairs and stood on the banisters. The view was perfect and if you were spotted you could easily get away. As I thought of it, I claimed first look.

The next Thursday afternoon, we told Mrs Evans we were all going to the bedroom to write letters. Then we heard Jenny come up the stairs and turn the taps on. As soon as she started to sing, we knew she was in the bath and we crept out of the room and I got up on the banisters. By golly Bill, you may have seen the Thames on fire but I wouldn't swop that for what I saw! She was lying in the bath facing me washing her breasts with a sponge—very slowly. Her breasts are really big with large brown nipples. I only wished it was me that was washing them. Then, without any warning, she suddenly stood up, and there was I looking straight at IT!!!!! I tell you Bill, I had such a shock I fell off the banisters. Mrs Evans called out and we all rushed outside.

Of course, the others were annoyed that they didn't get to have a look, so I had to describe everything I'd seen in great detail. Well, everyone knows about breasts but now I understand why they always paint IT out in those Health and Beauty magazines and statues of women never seem to have one at all. For a start IT is shaped like a triangle. And here's something you won't find in history books. IT is BLACK!!! When I told the others, Johnny called me a liar so I punched him on the nose. We puzzled about this for a long time and next Thursday Johnny is going to have a look to prove that I'm right. I think the whole thing is very peculiar.

We had a smashing fight with some of the local boys. They're quite tough and I think they'll come back. At least that's what they promised. It was all over our house in the woods. Oh yes, you don't know about that do you? I think it was Gavin's idea or it may have been Ronnie's. Anyway, it was certainly Ronnie who planned it all out. We thought that if we were going to fight the Nazis, it would be a good idea if we had a secret hide-out. Somewhere where we could leap out,

91

Ronnie Johnson showing his parents our hide-out in the woods

make a lightning strike and then disappear after we'd killed enough but before they could bring up reinforcements.

Right behind Machen House, outside the walls, there's a small wood. From there we can attack the house, the road and the station, so it's in a good position. We first of all found a thick clump of trees that was very overgrown. In the centre of this we dug out a six foot square about three foot deep. Then we built a roof with branches, covered it over with some canvas and camouflaged the whole lot with twigs and bits of bush. Inside, we've got water, a candle and a map. Outside, it's absolutely invisible. You can stand looking straight at it and not see it. We think this lot must have stumbled on it by accident. But when we found them, they were inside, claimed it was theirs and wouldn't come out. So that's when the battle started. Johnny was all for using our trusty bows straight off, but Charles said if we killed one of them we might end up getting expelled from school. After that it was stones, sticks and fists. Of course, being outside, we had more stones than they did, but even so they put up a good fight. It was only when Bob set light to it that they scarpered. Sometimes Bob really is a silly bugger. After we'd put the fire out, there wasn't much left of our secret house—and anyway, it wasn't a secret anymore, so I expect we'll build one somewhere else.

Not much else has happened down here. Everything is really peaceful, not like up in London. Gavin's sister arrives tomorrow. I hope she's like Gavin but with a name like Bridget I very much doubt it.

Keep on dodging the bombs.

Yours aye,

Merv

7, Nesbit Road,
Eltham, S.E.9.
20th September 1940

Dear Merv,

Another war communique from the front! Three nights ago, as I was sleeping in the Anderson, a tremendous crash woke me up. Dad said a really big one had dropped nearby. As we were still alive we all went back to sleep but in the morning we went off on our new hobby, bomb hunting. We didn't have to go far. Just around the corner, in Briset Road, a man shouted out to us and pointed up Brenley Gardens. 'There she is', he bawled, like Ahab sighting Moby Dick. We followed his directions and found an amazing scene of destruction.

A man standing outside his doorless and windowless house said that a landmine had been dropped by parachute. He said that the police at Shooters Hill station saw it floating down but thought it was a Nazi airman—quite a few of the 'master race' arrive in England by parachute these days! The crater was enormous. Altogether 14 houses were completely destroyed and at least 50 others uninhabitable. Yet an Anderson shelter quite near the crater was hardly touched. That's proof of their value, if ever there was one!

it seemed to them from where
they stood that the whole end
of the garden was one mass of
rubble. As they walked up the
garden John found a piece of,
what afterwards turned out to
be, a magnetic land-mine. A
man was standing at the entrance
of his windowpaneless and
doorless house and upon being
questioned he told them that
the thing that had caused the
damage was a magnetic land
mine which had been dropped
on a parachute. He said that
the police at the Shooters
Hill Station had seen it
coming down but they had
been mislead into thinking

The land-
mine in
Stanley

24

Account entry for 18th September 1940

94

I felt sorry for the people made homeless; thank God very few had been killed. One man was giving away tea and sugar. He said it was to stop looters getting it. Another said that he had wanted his suit pressed and now the Germans had done it for him, underneath what was left of his house. I saw a woman clambering over the wreckage of what used to be her home, trying to drag out anything she could find, a cup or a vase—anything. She never spoke nor took notice of anyone. I suppose she was still shocked. There was another bloke giving away tins of what he said the Germans had turned into stewed fruit. Apparently a gas main had burnt down his kitchen.

At this rate you will come back to find that Eltham has completely disappeared. No, don't worry, Kenward Road is still there, and so is our school. We're all hard at work. Lessons are more chaotic than usual, because every time the air raid warning goes, we're all sent out into the playground. I expect Haggar thinks this will make us a better target. I should think the school will have to close before long. If a big one did fall when we were all inside it could be very nasty. It will be a pity if it does close because we have a lot of laughs.

Which reminds me. You know that Dennis's the newsagents has an advert case outside, well the glass was broken, so we pinned up the following notice, 'Wanted. 5 chickens with 21 legs. Talking ones preferred.' We gave Alma Evans address. A lot of trouble has followed and questions are being asked. I've got the feeling that someone saw us do it, so at the moment we are all lying low. It would be a pity to be caned by Haggar during what Churchill has called 'our finest hour'.

It's funny how all this bombing, death and destruction makes you think of the future. Somehow you know that this is really historic. Well, at least I do. If I'd been at Waterloo, I'd have written it all down at the time. I don't mean, 'Had a good fight. We won, they lost', but things like what we had for tea and about the blister on my foot, that sort of thing. So, for this reason I've stopped working on my life of Napoleon and instead I'm writing a diary of the 'Blitz'. If I'm blown up, make sure you keep these letters. If the house is blown up, I keep the diary in a box under my bed.

By the way, I've started selling your silver paper pictures. I sold one for 2/6 and got orders worth 12/6. Is it alright if I pocket one fifth of the takings? I felt unwell today so I went to Dr. Evans. She told me that the Sick Club we belong to had not paid her anything for two years. So if the bombs do get me, I shall be a long time recovering. Oh yes, your black triangle. I've asked around and Potter says it's nothing but hair. His sister is seventeen. Even he hasn't seen IT. And what does 'yours aye' mean? Write soon,

Cheerio,
Bill

Machen House,
Lower Machen,
Monmouthshire.
30th September 1940

Dear Bill,

We've had a bomb! A few nights ago we were all woken up by our own local siren going off. This has never happened before. We've heard them in the distance of course, but as they only seem to bomb Cardiff or Newport nobody takes much notice. At first we couldn't hear anything at all and Johnny reckoned that some fool had switched it on by mistake. Then we heard this bomber. It was flying very low and sounded as though it was coming straight at us. It roared right over the house and then the bomb went off. The whole house shook and rattled. Obviously he was aiming for us and missed. And no one tried to shoot him down. Not surprising really as we haven't got any ack-ack guns near here, but if we had, they couldn't have missed. Of course, we wanted to go out straight away but Mrs Evans made us go back to bed. Next morning we all got up early for once. The bomb had fallen in the corner of a field about four hundred yards from the house, so I suppose you could call it 'a near miss'. For the amount of noise it made, the crater wasn't all that big—about fifty feet across and ten feet deep. Ronnie says the bomb was probably a fifty pounder. We hunted around for shrapnel but couldn't find a single piece, then a policeman turned up and told us to clear off because he was going to guard it. Why guard a hole in the ground? Who was going to steal it?

Gavin's sister, Bridget arrived ten days ago. She's tall, slim, has long legs, jet black hair and is very beautiful. She's absolutely smashing and joins in everything. I think I told you that there's a ten foot wall that runs all around the grounds. One of our favourite dares, is to run along the top of the wall as fast as we can. It's only nine inches wide and if you come off there's quite a drop. Heather and Rosemary don't do this, but as soon as Bridget arrived she was 'running the wall', as we call it, with the rest of us.

Bridget and I get on very well together. I still like Joan Longley, but I think I'm in love with Bridget. Of course, I haven't told her this, or any of the others. You're the only one who knows, so keep it quiet. One day we sat up on the roof of the tower for about an hour together. I told her how you could see for miles and took her up there. Only the two of us. We just sat and talked. It was smashing. And on another day, when we were out with the others, we hid in a cave. That's when

Bridget Young

Gavin Young aged 9, with his mother

97

I almost kissed her. But while I was thinking about it, we heard this rumbling noise. It sounded as though the cave was falling in and we rushed outside. It was just a flock of sheep charging over the top of the cave. I really cursed those sheep, because the others spotted us and I'd lost my one big chance.

Bridget and Gavin have now left to go back to school and so have the girls, and Machen House is now ours again. It all seems a bit empty without them.

Ronnie Johnson had a go at us the other day, saying that we've been down here all this time and apart from going to school, we haven't been out of the grounds. Of course, this wasn't Ronnie talking; his mother and sister, Olive, had just been down to see him, so it really came from them. Anyway, he got us all organised and that morning we walked to Caerphilly and back which is a good twelve miles. When we did get there, the only thing worth looking at was a castle but the bloody place was locked up, so we couldn't even get into it. That afternoon, he said we should go and see Ruperra castle so we all set off—but this time on our bikes. Near a village called Draethen, we crossed a river that was pure black. I suppose it must have come from a coal mine. Be a waste of time fishing in water like that. Then we had a hell of a climb, but when we got to the top the view was worth it. You could see way over towards Cardiff on one side and Caerphilly on the other. But the important thing was, we found a memorial to a soldier called Lieutenant Griffiths who had been killed in the Charge of the Light Brigade. When we got back we asked Mrs Evans about it and she said he was related to Captain Griffiths—she never calls him Colonel. So we are living with quite a famous family.

All of us have got our bikes down here now which means we can get to school in fifteen minutes. When we had to walk the four miles to Rhiwderin it used to take us nearly an hour. Coming home there's a big long hill and we race each other down it. Bob's got a speedo and says we go at up to 30mph!

Miss Pitts really doesn't like me and for an English teacher she's absolutely rotten. All she seems to know about are pronouns, synonyms and syntax. She hates it when she has to give me nine out

98

Our class at 'Rude Herring' (Rhiwderin), 1940. Merv, back row, 5th left;
Ronnie, 3rd row, 4th left; 'Zasu' Pitts on left

of ten for an essay—I've never had ten from her yet. She gave Joan ten the other day because she said it was written in such beautiful copperplate it was a joy to read. I bet your Miss Wilcox wouldn't care a bugger what an essay looked like if it was a good one. I'll tell you how stupid she is, Bill. This term we're doing Henry the Fifth and I started off reading the Chorus—'Oh for a Muse of fire'. Here's a bloke telling the audience what it's all about and how they are going to have to use their imaginations a bit because they can't have horses and battles on the stage. It's a good speech and I really let rip. At the end of it she said, 'There's no need to be so dramatic, Mervyn.' I ask you?

The whole class has been shuffled around this term. I used to sit at the front but now I'm right at the back. This is probably because Miss Pitts wants to see as little of me as possible. The trouble is, I can't see the board properly. When I asked old Morgan if he could write bigger, he said, 'No, you concentrate harder.' Stupid sod.

As I copied 'yours aye' from Gavin and forgot to ask him what it meant, I'll sign off as usual,

Your friend,

Merv

7, Nesbit Road,
Eltham, S.E.9.
16th October 1940

Dear Merv,

Had a close shave yesterday! With no school to go to, I've been playing tennis with Alma Evans, who is often eager for a beating. The siren went and so Alma buzzed off home. These days it goes so often that nobody pays any attention until the bombers get close. Anyway, about four o'clock I was coming down Well Hall Parade when I heard the loud whistle of a bomb. I jumped off my bike, let it fall and dived down beside it. So did everybody else. Crash followed crash, four in all, and as the ground shook, dirt, dust and stones fell on us. God, it must be near, I thought! When it all quietened down, we all got up, dusted ourselves and looked around. A huge black cloud was rolling up into the sky from the direction of Westmount Road. (That will give you an idea of how near it was!) I was just about to go to find out the damage when a nosey parker Warden herded me and about twenty others into a shelter. I only stayed about two minutes, just long enough for him to push off. Then I went on a bomb hunt.

It's not difficult to find a bomb which has landed nearby. First, you ride towards the smoke. Then you see shuffled tiles on roofs and muck and rubbish all over the road. By the time you come to broken windows and doors you're almost there. Other tell-tale signs are smashed fencing, telephone poles with wires down and water gushing from broken mains. This crater was not as large as the one in Brenley Gardens but it was big. (Certainly bigger than the one you had in Wales.) Luckily nobody had been hurt as the house that had been hit was empty at the time. Neighbours were out sweeping up glass and seemed to treat the whole thing as a good excuse for a chat. One bloke was running around with a kettle and teapot trying to find some clean running water. As he said, you can't have the Germans stopping afternoon tea.

Being off school is a bore. I found myself a job last Sunday. Dad, and some of the other men at the Library where he works, were asked to deal with bomb damage and make an Inventory of all the furniture and who it belonged to. Dad said I could go along. At first we stood about in Wellington Street, near Woolwich Library, chatting to the driver and a team who had brought a large moving van for the job. Eventually a warden arrived and said that a big bomb had fallen during the night, killing six people and wrecking a number of houses. Our job was to interview the survivors to see what they wanted done with their furniture. If it was to be moved then we were to make two lists, with the help of carbon paper, give one to them and the other to the driver to take to the Rest Centre.

We arrived at Jackson Street, Plumstead (up near the Common) to find an awful mess. Dad told me to be careful of what I said in case I met some poor devil who had just lost a relative. It certainly turned out to be a muddle in every way! One poor sod said he would go, then changed his mind and said he would rather live in the wreckage than a Rest Centre. I can't say I blame him. Two other blokes let their wives decide for them. The wives said 'no', then the men said 'yes', but the wives got their way. I was puzzled by what to call some of the pieces of furniture. You had to get it right because later it would all have to be identified. Luckily, when I was stuck, the furniture men always knew the proper names for things.

The first family I dealt with consisted of an old man and his wife, his son and daughter-in-law. They kept on arguing and changing their minds and making a mess of my precious lists. Thus, after I'd put down 5 chairs, they told me they'd made a mistake and it was 4. I cross out 5 and put 4. They said they'd send 3 to the Rest Centre and 1 to some relative who lived in Welling. Then they discovered they owned another chair, making it 5. The father seemed surprised to see it and said he'd lived in the house for twenty-five years. So then they decided to put 4 in store and send one to the relative in Welling. More argument. It all ended up, about six sheets of paper later, with them sending 3 to Welling and 2 to the Rest Centre.

It's easy to be angry but how would you feel if your home had been blown to bits and you had to make a quick decision?

Personally, I think they'll be lucky to see their stuff again anyway. Dad and I spent a lot of time clambering over the rubble trying to

boss and he gave me number 10
to do. At first I was a
little perplexed at the strange
articles of furniture that emerged
from the houses: things which
defied my powers of classification
However the furniture man; knew
the proper names & it was alright
The first family was an elderly
man and his wife, and his son
and daughter in law. They caused
a lot of crossing out in my
book owing to their indecision,
thus:- I put down, "Five Chairs"
they have only 4, I cross out.
They decide to have 3 stored, I a
again cross out. Then they
discover they have five after
all and they will have 2
stored. And so it goes on. —

Entry from Bill's diary, 18th October 1940

salvage anything that was intact. When we did, we tried to find out who it belonged to. All the time the Salvation Army van fed us cups of tea. We went to Aunt Ada's for dinner, walking across the Common to Abbey Wood. More cups of tea, then back to make another inventory.

It was then that I had the strangest experience of the day. A talkative old lady, hiding in the ruins, shouted out descriptions of the most weird things. I filled up four pages but she just went on and on calling out all sorts of things. Finally I called a halt and marched into the ruins to talk to her. Poor woman, I felt so sorry for her. Her husband had been killed in the night and she had come back from the mortuary in the dinner break. No wonder that none of us could find any of these weird and wonderful objects she'd been calling out. The answer was that she'd just been babbling, probably talking about things she might have owned years before. In the end we phoned for an ambulance to take her away.

Once the van was full we set off. We didn't go to a Rest Centre after all, but to the Palace Cinema in the High Street. This is now a warehouse. Best thing for it. As you know, it always showed lousy films and I usually got the seat with the stone pillar in front of it. We got washed in the Women's lav. The Gents wasn't working. The men stood outside to warn off any females, then the women took over and warned the men off. Back home, mum had kept our meal hot, so we had a second dinner for tea.

I'm a bit out of touch with school, but I hear that two Central School kids have been killed. Brothers named Williams. I didn't know them as they were in a lower class. If the school had been open, I expect Haggar would have had a service or something for them. I wonder what harm those poor buggers had done to those Nazi bastards?

You say you are in love. I bet that in six months time you won't be able to say that. At least, not about the same girl. Probably because you're in such a dizzy state, you forgot to answer my question about the silver paper pictures. Don't worry, I made the decision for you. I've taken my 3/- and enclose a P.O. for 12/-.

Cheerio, Bill

Machen House,
Lower Machen,
Monmouthshire.
3rd November 1940

Dear Bill,

You certainly seem to be having a tough time of it back at Eltham. Down here, not much is happening at all. Before I forget, thanks for the 12/- and do you still have anymore pictures to sell? I only ask because Christmas is getting close.

With Gavin and the girls back at school, we don't seem to have much fun anymore. Charles says it's only natural to feel fed up at this time of year because the days are still getting shorter and that everyone used to celebrate Christmas in ancient times not for any religious reason, but because the days had started to grow longer. I think he's probably right because he does read a lot. Another thing I didn't know, was that he and Gavin write to one another. I suppose it's not so surprising as they always used to have long discussions together.

Since I last wrote to you I've had a bit of an accident. It wasn't much really, but it was what happened afterwards that caused the problem. As you know, we all go to school on our bikes. My bike really needed new brakes because the rear cable had broken and I couldn't get a new one. Then Bob came up with the answer. We took off the front cable and fitted it to the rear brake. The trouble was, the cable wasn't long enough to reach the handlebars, so we fixed the brake handle to the crossbar and it worked a treat. That was on the Sunday.

Monday morning we were all late starting for school and tore off down the drive like dirt-track riders. Of course, I've never told you what it's like outside the grounds, have I? Well, right opposite the drive gates is the village Post Office and store, so it's a sharp turn to the left, which means if you're going fast, as we always are, you have to brake hard. The others were ahead of me and I was pedalling furiously to catch up. As I got to the gates, without thinking, I squeezed at the handlebars. Nothing happened!! And standing to the side of the shop was a bloody horse and cart and I was hurtling straight towards the Post Office window!! I threw myself off the bike and bounced across the road bashing my head on the cartwheel. I think I was knocked out but I can't be sure.

Anyway, when I got up the others had gone and no one had come to my rescue! I thought that was pretty rotten. So, when I finally limped into school, the knees of my trousers were torn and there was blood everywhere. Naturally I thought I'd be treated the same as a wounded soldier would have been. Not a bit of it. Old Morgan said that if I only got up in the morning, none of this would have happened and promptly gave me a hundred lines for being late. It wasn't until the break, when Joan suggested to Morgan that I went to the doctor in case I got lockjaw, that the old sod let me go. 'Lockjaw for some people would be a blessing', he said, smiling at me.

It was at the doctors that the real trouble began though. There was only one really bad cut on my knee, the rest were just grazes. It didn't stop him going over the whole lot with iodine and that really hurt. As soon as he'd bandaged me up, I thanked him and started to go, but he hadn't finished by a long way. Weight, height, hearing and an eye-test. That's when I found out that I was short-sighted. No wonder I've never been able to see things in the distance. Anyway, this doctor sent me along to an optician who fitted me out with a pair of glasses that look bloody awful. I expect Mum will get a shock because he's sent her the bill.

When I got back to school there was a lot of giggling from the girls, which you would expect, but when Andrews called me 'foureyes', there was nothing I could do except thump him. It was a good punch and got him square on the nose which started to bleed—and would you believe it, that's when Miss Pitts came in. I had to walk all the way to Bassaleg where old Grindle gave me six of the best and warned me that he'd be keeping an eye on me in future. As Bassaleg is about two miles from Rhiwderin, he's obviously got better eyesight than I have. By the time I'd got back to school it was almost time to go home. That wasn't a very good Monday.

Mum, Dad and Vevlie are moving up to North Wales this week. Dad is going to be foreman of a factory and Vev is working for Lord Woolton at the Ministry of Food. Perhaps we'll all get more to eat

105

now. Eric hasn't been called up yet because he's doing important war work at Woolwich Arsenal, so I expect he'll stay on at Kenward Road on his own. If he does, he'll probably get his own back on Dad. Every Spring, Dad goes around the garden painting all the rocks in the rockery, white—plus any other stone he can find. Eric shouts at him and says he's turning the place into a bloody barracks. I imagine that next Spring Eric will go around and scrub every rock clean.

For your information, yes, I am still in love with Bridget. I have the feeling that Johnny Jackson has guessed and told Joan because she's suddenly become very friendly. Anyway, that's all the news from down here.

Your friend,
Merv

Eric posing by runner beans and
Dad's painted white rocks

7, Nesbit Road,
Eltham, S.E.9.
25th November 1940

Dear Merv,

Being off school has set me thinking of the good times I had last summer before the bombers came. After all, my last few letters have been so full of the war, I haven't given you any school news. So here it is—six months late!

We had an exciting cricket season. I tried to put my Uncle Fred's theories into practice; you know, he's the one who played for Kent. Our fiercest match was against the Elementary scruffs. One of the boys, a big sod called Coppernob because of his hair, can bowl like hell. I stood up to his fast bowling by stone-walling as much as I could. Once I hit out and scored four. This was the second highest score of our team so you'll gather we didn't do too well. In another match we got the Elementary out for 1. Yes, all of them! We scored 33 and I stayed in all the time for 2. When I told my Uncle, he said that staying in for the whole match was fine, but he didn't think much of my score. I reminded him that even Walter Hammond and Hutton were sometimes out for 2. He was forced to agree on this point, but mentioned that they might have been facing a slightly higher class of bowling. You've never mentioned cricket in your letters. Too busy with bows and arrows I suppose. Archery can hardly be classed as a national sport, now can it?

Something else I forgot to tell you. I was elected School Captain. This only came about because Haggar took a sudden liking to the idea of democracy. Of course, as soon as I gave him the joyful news he promptly abandoned all thoughts of democracy and told the School Council that they must think again. So now Jones is School Captain. You probably remember him because he was evacuated to Deal for a few months. He's completely useless being both mentally and physically weak. I think I might have stayed as Captain but for the 'Odeon Affair', as we nicknamed it. You know the Odeon next to the school? Well, every Monday morning, one of the attendants comes out with a ladder and a bag full of metal letters, climbs up and

107

carefully puts up the name of the new film. I often stand and watch because he always gets it wrong and when I point it out, he swears at me like mad. This particular week his spelling was worse than usual and he ended up with, 'The Grate Ditactor'. So I waited until he had climbed down and was all packed up ready to go in, then I told him. He jumped up and down in fury then marched in to complain to Haggar—who called me an intellectual snob (me?) and gave me one on each hand.

The only other thing of interest that happened last term was that we had a school concert. You would have liked it, being as you are so fond of the theatre and acting and all that. I wrote a play about Cromwell which was acted badly by idiots who couldn't remember their lines. They needed you, Merv, the great actor, to show them the way. Following in Shaw's footsteps, I wrote a preface which I was allowed to read to a bored audience. 'I am not one of those people who believe it is wrong to kill a king', I announced to a crowd of grim looking, patriotic parents! I then went on to read out a list of all the kings I thought should have been killed. They were, William II (who was), Henry I, Richard I, (who was), John, Edward II (who was), Richard II (who was), Richard III (who was), Henry VIII, Mary Tudor, James I, Charles I (who was), Charles II, James II, George III and George IV. As I read out this list, many people started to laugh. I can only suppose they thought I was joking.

What's the food like at your end? It's getting worse here. Dad says that at the rate we're going, we'll be lucky to have shepherd's pie for Christmas dinner. Last week we were lucky and had a bit of mutton. Have you had spam yet? I think it's one of the good things that have come out of this rotten war. I had some at a wedding in June. It's much better than ham and you can fry it and mince it up as well. Have you heard the joke about the people queueing up for sausages? A woman comes up and asks, 'Are you in the queue for bread or sausages?' 'Dunno' says another woman, 'They're both the same anyway.' Since the school was closed, I sometimes have a meal in Lyons. The last time I had fish, which tasted foul and was tough as old boot leather. As the knife was blunt I had trouble trying to cut it, and in the end the whole lot ended up in my lap.

I'm told that last night was very eventful. Dozens of bombs fell and one set light to the pavilion in Eltham Park. We have all given up sleeping in the Anderson now that winter's come. Much too cold and damp. Dad says we might as well die in comfort. In any case, I think it would have killed my mother to sleep outside in wintertime. Her heart attacks get worse, what with the bombs, shells and all the noise. Lately I have been sleeping through quite a lot of excitement, including the complete destruction of the Health Centre on the corner of Westhorne Avenue and Briset Road. This was terrible because about seven nurses were killed. Two Sundays ago a bomb landed in Lionel Road about mid-day. I saw the poor devils being carried out of the wreckage. Their faces were all blackened. A little girl was killed in this house. Her neck was broken when a wall fell on her. All this damage is done by the odd bomber creeping over when it's rainy or at night. The buggers don't fly up the river on parade as they used to. They're scared of our fighters.

Courtesy of Greater London Record Office

A night raid on London, November, 1940

There are rumours of the school re-opening after Christmas. I hope so because if they wait for the war to end I could be an old man with a white beard before I take my School Cert. We were given plenty of homework when we left. I finished my History and English long ago, but of course, I don't do French and Maths on principle. I found out that Haggar is a Maths genius, which explains why he doesn't appreciate me. I'm quite sure he'd never even heard of some of the Kings on my Execution List.

I went up to London to buy some books in Charing Cross Road. By God, Merv, talk about 'Knocked 'em in the Old Kent Road.' They've certainly had a pasting around there, poor sods. Between St Johns and London Bridge there are huge areas where there's not a house standing—just piles and piles of rubble. And walking between Oxford Circus and Tottenham Court Road, every single shop was damaged. Of course, most of them display, 'Business as Usual' but the sign I liked best was, 'More Open Than Usual.' This is the first time I've been up to Town since the raids so it was quite a shock. Thousands of people spend their nights in the Underground. There are bunks against the walls and I had to step over people who were sleeping. And this was during the day. I suppose they were fire-watchers or wardens trying to catch up on their sleep. There were also quite a few things written up on the walls, but I think Hitler would need to be a double-jointed acrobat to follow some of the suggestions!!! In Charing Cross Road they have 3d and 6d stalls outside the bookshops and I picked up some really good bargains.

Mum has just told me that my favourite meal is ready—sausage, pork and beans, potatoes and currant pudding with condensed milk. Quite a feast. It's not even anyone's birthday. I wonder how long she had to queue for all that?

Cheerio,
Bill

110

Machen House,
Lower Machen,
1st December 1940

Dear Bill,

Didn't you know that Kenward Road had been bombed? It happened on November 11th—Armistice Day!! Eric came down last week-end. He said he'd been so busy cleaning up the house that he could do with a rest and a bit of peace and quiet. I thought he'd come to see me. Anyway, I suppose I'd better tell you all about it. If you're going to write a History of the War, facts like this will come in useful, so here's how it all happened.

As you know, Eric works in the Danger Buildings in Woolwich Arsenal. He said that the bombing there had been terrible. In one raid, 48 bombs had landed close by him. It was so bad, he got on his motorbike and got the hell out of it. When he went back the next day, the place where he was sheltering had been flattened. They work a twenty-four hour shift system now and he'd been working at night. On the morning of the 11th, he'd come home and had his breakfast when the siren went. He didn't pay much attention and decided that before he went down into the shelter, he'd have a shave. Just as well! He was at the sink in the kitchen shaving when the bomb dropped. He didn't hear it coming at all. He says that when you're right underneath it, you don't hear a thing. You only hear the scream of a bomb if it's going to miss you.

The next thing he knew, was that he found himself under the kitchen table, pots and pans flying around, the window caved in and the room so thick with soot that he could hardly see. All he knew was that he was alive and the house was still standing—but he wasn't sure for how long—so he got out into the garden as fast as he could.

All the windows at the back of the house were out and most of the tiles were off the roof. Dad's shed was leaning sideways and there were piles of earth and uprooted plants all over the lawn and the clothes post was down. Of course the first thing Eric did was to go to the little shed, where he keeps his motorbike, to see if the Black Panther was alright. Luckily it was. When he got to the end of the

111

garden, he realised what a narrow escape he'd had. The shelter had received a direct hit and was just a tangled mass of torn metal at the bottom of a fifteen foot crater! If he hadn't decided to shave first, Eric would have been mixed up with all that lot. And if Mum, Dad and Vevlie hadn't gone to North Wales, which was only a few days before, Mum would certainly have been in that shelter and would be dead by now!!!

And here's another incredible thing. A week before they left, Dad said he wasn't going to use the shelter anymore. He'd had a dream about it being blown up. Mum and Vev just laughed at him and went on using the shelter while Dad slept in the house. On the day he left, Dad repeated his warning to Eric, but of course, Eric kept on using it. He said he was foolish not to have listened to Dad because once when they were up in London together Dad had another premonition which saved both their lives. It was during a raid. They were running to shelter in the Underground when Dad stopped dead in his tracks. He pulled Eric back and insisted they went into the crypt under St. Martin's in the Field. When they came out they found that a bomb had landed at the entrance to that very tube station and masses of people had been killed. Dad said he could SEE it all happening!!! I wasn't a bit surprised when Eric told me because funny things like that do happen to Dad. Once when we were on holiday, he woke up swearing that he'd been bitten by a monkey. Mum laughed and said it was just a dream, but on his arm were a small set of teeth-marks. And both Mum and Dad have false teeth which they take out at night. Bet you can't explain that!

Eric took a fortnight off work to get everything cleared up. Apart from the fence at the end of the garden which is still down, he says you'd never know a bomb had fallen. We've also got a new dug-out. This one is right outside the back door, so it's well protected against blast. Eric dug the hole himself and the Council did the concreting and put the shelter in. It's much deeper than the other one and the top is all covered with earth, which Eric says he'll plant with flowers in the spring. He's got carpet on the floor, two bunk beds and an oil lamp and says it's very cosy now.

Eric's motorbike by the new Anderson shelter ·

He's also lashed out and bought a new radio which is all electric. Now that he's on his own he can't be bothered to change the accumulators every week. That was always my job to take them to the shop by Well Hall station. It used to cost 9d to charge them, so that will be quite a saving over the year. It's called a McMichael and you can listen in to stations all over the world. He's also fixed up a speaker in the kitchen and by flicking a switch, you can hear it in either room separately or in both together. With the old set, the only way to hear it in the kitchen, was to turn it up loud in the front room, which always annoyed the neighbours. So, one way or another, that bomb has brought quite a few changes to Kenward Road.

Oh yes, one important fact I've missed out is that the raid on Kenward Road was carried out by the Italians. This was the very first time that they've raided England. Trust them to choose Armistice Day. Mum has never liked the Wops. When I was small, we used to have three ice-cream men who came round. One was Walls, the other Eldorado and the third one was an Italian. Mum called him the hokey-pokey man and we never had ice-cream from him because (according to Mum), he kept the ice-cream under his bed. When the Italians used mustard gas in Abyssinia, people used to throw stones at him. We never saw him after that so I suppose he went back to Italy. Perhaps he joined their Air Force just in order that he could come back and drop a bomb on Kenward Road.

I don't use my glasses at all now. I really looked awful. I tell you this, I'm never going to poke fun at kids who do have to wear them. I find that if I put both hands to my forehead, as though I'm concentrating, pull my eyes sideways, so that I look like a Chink, I can see the board fairly well. The only danger is, I could end up looking Chinese. Still, I could always play the part of Doctor Fu Man Chu, couldn't I?

After Eric had gone back on Sunday, I went to sing in the choir as usual. Actually, I quite enjoy it now. By golly, Bill, I bet you never thought you'd see the day when I went to church TWICE on 'a Sunday!

Anyway, the vicar said that the electric motor for the organ had packed up and that Johnny and I had to stand behind it and pump it by hand. Well, we started off well enough but Johnny soon got bored so we decided to play noughts and crosses on the wall. We were scoring pretty even, then he began to get ahead which annoyed me. I was concentrating so hard, that with one hymn, they'd sung the whole of the first verse before I realised the organist was hissing at us like mad to start pumping. To make matters worse, with this same hymn, I thought they'd finished when there was still one verse to go. The vicar really lashed into us, especially when he saw all the noughts and crosses over his whitewashed wall. Neither of us got our usual sixpence. Christmas is coming but I'm not looking forward to it. Won't be as good as last year and in spite of all the bombs I wish I could spend it at home.

Your friend,
Merv

7, Nesbit Road,
Eltham, S.E.9.
1st January 1941

Dear Merv,

Happy New Year! It seems an age since we last met and it's well over a month since I wrote to you. I had to go back and read your last letter to see if you had written anything of great importance. I needn't have bothered. No, seriously though, thanks for your account of the bombing of Kenward Road. From now on, when I hear a bomb screaming down at me, I will comfort myself that you've told me it can't possibly have my number on it. I only hope to God that you're brother Eric, is right!

Actually I didn't hear about your house being bombed until quite some time afterwards. I expect Churchill himself made sure that no one knew about it just in case Mussolini started to get above himself. The fact that the Haisman family are still alive and well, will I am sure, be a great disappointment to the Italian High Command.

I hope your Christmas wasn't as bad as you thought it was going to be, because you sounded really down in the dumps. Just to cheer you up, I passed on some of your news to the girls. They even remembered you, and a few—the blind and the stupid—wished that you were back here. Probably want to get even for what you did to them at Deal!!!

I've heard that the school is going to open again this term, which means that in spite of all the slaughter and destruction, I shall only have lost one term. Unless of course, it has to close again. Are you still studying for the Oxford School Certificate down there, or have you changed to one with some weird Welsh university?

I think my memories of this Christmas will be of fog! Every time dad and I went up the baths it was foggy. I also said goodbye to Uncle Will in a thick fog just before Christmas. He was called up and came to say cheerio to mum and dad. Mum was very upset—after all, he's her only brother—but dad never did like him. He's a strange chap because no sooner had he arrived, than he took mum and me off to the cinema. Afterwards, I offered to walk up the road with him. He was very pleased and thought that I was going because of him. I hadn't the heart to tell him I'd planned to see Smithson anyway. So we walked along in the freezing cold and he was grateful and I felt awful, as though I'd deceived him in some way. Being a romantic, I watched him disappear in the swirling fog thinking that it might be for the last time. (Which it might!)

The Saturday before Christmas was memorable! I know that with you it's Sundays, but I now have a great liking for Saturdays. This is probably because of the description in 'Tom Sawyer' of his delight at being free from school and being able to do what he wanted. I feel just the same.

Well, this particular Saturday was special because it was the last before Christmas. I cycled around Blackfen. It was cold, clear and bright—the fog having lifted—then I called on Smithson and suggested a game of tennis. Naturally the courts were closed so we climbed over the wire. It was a very funny feeling playing tennis on a winter's day with gloves on!

Afterwards we cycled up to Blackheath pond where some small boys were trying to get a large, steam model boat to work. For a long time it refused to move and just gave out clouds of steam. Then one boy took the funnel off to fiddle with the engine, but before he could get it on again, it shot off, then stopped. One chap with wellingtons, waded in after it. He got the funnel on and got it going. The boat sailed out right into the middle of the pond and promptly stopped again. It just sat there with steam pouring out of it. As you know, the pond is only really deep in the middle—right where the boat was. By now, quite a large crowd of 'expert engineers' had gathered and started to argue on the best way to rescue the boat. The proud owner was in tears because the boat actually belonged to his father who was in the Navy—I only hope he isn't a stoker. We had a good laugh watching them throw stones to create ripples. Just as we were leaving, two boys staggered over and threw in a manhole cover. This created such a tidal wave that the boat sank. On the way home, we decided that the boat would be a non-floating war memorial to whoever was going to fall down that open manhole.

I spent Christmas Eve at Smithson's house. We played whist with his

Trams that did not "have some fun in the morning".
Abbey Wood Tram Depot, bombed 7th November, 1940

Courtesy of London Transport Museum

parents and his father gave us some beer. He said it was a special sort. I don't know what it was, but I certainly could get to like it. I had quite a few and I left their house well after midnight, feeling quite light-headed, and began singing at the top of my voice. Near the 'Yorkshire Grey', I stumbled over a park bench, which I set over the tramlines so that the trams could have some fun in the morning. Back home, I took my shoes off before I crept into the house. I'd seen so many drunks doing it in funny films that it seemed the right thing to do. Then I played Father Christmas to mum and dad, which was a bit of a change round. After that, I staggered off to bed. In the morning, when dad came in to give me my present—a shirt—I had a really bad headache, which made dad roar with laughter. He said, 'The first of many. Come on, hair of the dog.' Then he took me to the Yorkshire Grey, where he was convinced I'd spent a wild evening. He brought me out a Brown Ale and made me drink it. I drank it very slowly, feeling sick all the time.

The bombers still come over. A couple of weeks ago, a Jerry dropped an oil bomb. It doesn't make a deep crater but sprays oil all over the place. I think it's supposed to be dropped into the middle of a raging fire once a raid has got things going. I saw a little boy who lives near here, dragging away a large, tangled and jagged piece of this bomb as a souvenir—all of it, dripping with thick, black oil.

I followed him to find out what he was going to do with it. He managed to get it into his kitchen before his mum found out. Poor little sod. His mum screamed blue murder at him and his dad gave him a good hiding for messing up the kitchen.

I was going to see 'Gone with the Wind' but they wanted 2/6 to get in because it's such a long film. Well, I reckon Clark Gable is worth 3d, Vivien Leigh 1/- (because she's so pretty), Leslie Howard 6d and Olivia thingy absolutely nothing. Adding that lot up, I shan't go to see it until I can get in for 1/9. I did go to the Granada in Woolwich. I don't like going there because you always have to listen to that bloody awful electric organ in the interval. This time, as soon as the organist had risen up out of the depths, they flashed up the Air Raid Warning sign. Straight away the organ went down again, pink lights and all. I shouted out, 'Coward!!'. Everyone laughed but the manager threw me out.

Cheerio,
Bill

Machen House,
Lower Machen,
Monmouthshire.
9th January 1941

Dear Bill,

Thanks for your letter as it helped to cheer me up. I'm afraid that all of us are feeling a bit down in the dumps at the moment. Christmas wasn't as bad as I thought it was going to be. We had chicken for dinner—but of course, no sloe gin this year. In the afternoon we were

118

taken to the drawing room and had tea with the Griffiths but no one played games or anything like that, so it was all a bit boring.

The summer school holidays were fine because we were outside for most of the day, but this winter is so bloody cold and dreary, we spend a lot of our time indoors. Still, Mum has written from Llandudno Junction to say that they want me to come up there for Easter, so that's something to look forward to.

We don't do too badly for food down here. I think Mrs Evans knows a poacher so we get a lot of rabbit, either stewed or roast, which is my favourite. Of course, trying to get sweets is a waste of time. Oh yes, talking of food, have you ever had pheasant? Take a tip from me, don't bother. Some time before Christmas, the Colonel had some guests for dinner and Mrs Evans cooked pheasants' legs coated with mustard. There were a couple over and she asked me if I'd like a taste.

I had one mouthful and was nearly sick. The meat was rotten and really stank to high Heaven. Mrs Evans said that was because it was well hung and it had to be a bit 'high'. I wouldn't even give meat like that to a dog. Another thing, Stilton. It's a cheese and it smells like bad socks and has maggots crawling in it. I asked Mrs Evans if she was going to throw it away and she sounded quite shocked. 'Goodness gracious no, it's beautifully ripe.' I tell you Bill, if being rich means you have to eat food like that, I think I'll stay poor and live longer.

Gavin came for a short while but he's gone back now. A pity, because we always have a lot of fun when he's around. No sign of Bridget though. It's obvious her parents have decided to keep us apart. While he was here, we had a good fight with some of the local lads. They kept on climbing over the wall, throwing stones and running away, so we decided to lay an ambush. Charles climbed a tree to tell us which part of the wall they were planning to climb and we spread out either side of them. Just as they were about to climb up, we leapt over the wall and surrounded them. It was one hell of a fight, but as we were attacking on both fronts we had the advantage and soon had them on the run. They haven't been back since.

Old Lady Walker has said that she can't look after Charles anymore, so he's going to have to move to somewhere else. We're all feeling pretty rotten about him leaving.

Johnny and Bob were up at the quarry the other day and came back with a detonator—at least, that's what Ronnie says it was. They said they found it on the ground but I reckon they pinched it. Anyway, we wanted to try it out, so we took it into the woods and buried it. Then we lit the fuse and ran off. Nothing happened and Johnny said it must have gone out, so he went back to light it again. Just as he got there, it did go off! A hell of a bang with earth flying everywhere. Johnny ended up on his back covered in muck. Of course, we all roared with laughter, but Johnny lay on the ground for a good ten minutes, swearing like a trooper. I don't think he's planning on any more explosions. I expect you wouldn't mind giving up explosions as well.

That's about all that's been happening down here lately. As you can see, it's all a bit boring. Hope to have some brighter news in my next letter. Write soon.

Your friend,
Merv

7, Nesbit Road,
Eltham, S.E.9.
5th February 1941

Dear Merv,

Sorry to hear that you are having such a boring time down there, but then that's what happens to country bumpkins. Are you having a tough winter? We are. There seems to be snow all the time, which annoys me as I can't ride my bike to school. I don't like snow fights, but on my way home the other day, I came across two of our junior boys who were heavily outnumbered by girls from our class. They called to me for help so I had to join in. I hid behind a concrete tank trap, then suddenly sprang out scoring two direct hits. The girls hit back, so I fell down and let out some awful groans. At first they paid no attention. Then they came over to see if I was hurt—have you noticed how curious girls are? As soon as they were standing over me, I threw handfuls of snow up their skirts! Did they yell! They swore they would put snow down my trousers, so I fled—or, as they say in the papers—made a tactical withdrawal.

Next morning at Assembly, we had a lecture from Haggar about snow fighting. I think that one of the girls with cold, wet knickers— probably Margaret Radford—had moaned to Mrs Boon, who'd passed on this piece of good news to Haggar. Apparently, you should never throw ice, only snow, carefully examined to make sure there are no stones. You should not throw really hard. You should not (looking straight at me), play nasty, filthy tricks. And to actually throw snowballs at a girl was the same as hitting her. I ask you!!

We made a really good slide in the playground and when we went in for lessons, covered it with snow. When we came out for the break, there was old Tom, the caretaker, heading straight for it. He came a real cropper. When we helped him up, he said how surprised he was to have fallen down. So I asked him if he'd ever heard of the well known law of gravity. He tried to clip my ear, but as he was still standing on the slide, he promptly fell over again!

Do you have 'Warship Weeks'? Recently the local National Savings Committee offered a prize of 15/- for the best limerick about saving. I won it with the following immortal lines—worthy of Keats.

> There was a young lady named Hilda,
> Saw a hat in a shop and it thrilled her,
> But her mother, quite grave,
> Said, why don't you save,
> And help buy a Waltzing Matilda.

Haggar sent for me—always unsettling—and said how pleased he was I had won it. Honour of the school and all that rot. Then he asked me why I had written about a tank during 'Warship Week'. I thought of all sorts of smart cracks but kept my mouth shut. This pleased him. You have to be careful. Being a mathematician, he has no sense of humour at all, and of course, he hates me. I'd been chosen by the class

121

to speak to him about being let off woodwork, so thinking this might be a good moment, I asked him. Haggar thought about this, then looking lovingly at the three canes on his coat-rack, said he liked wood! He certainly makes good use of it because I've felt them all. Then he said that in place of woodwork, we could go to singing lessons. I was horrified until I remembered that we've now got a new singing teacher.

Miss Loams is young and lovely—a real 'pin-up' with gorgeous golden hair. She sometimes wears a very smart pleated skirt. Mum says this is very rare these days because it uses up so much material. She has dainty, high heeled shoes and these look lovely as she uses the pedals. Believe me, when she gets us to sing 'My Old Kentucky Home', we lads are almost in tears. The girls say she shouldn't have such dainty shoes in wartime. This is the very first time they've shown any interest in the war, although I often try to explain tactics to them and point out the various battle-fronts. Of course, the girls are just plain jealous. When I pointed out that Miss Loams was a lady and they were just kids, this nearly ended my friendship with Lucinda. The result is, that the girls play her up and get punished while we stand around like 'Little Lord Fauntleroys'. In fact, Haggar marched in the other day to say how pleased he was with the boys, which only proves that miracles can happen.

I went to Woolwich to see a parade of soldiers, airmen, ATS and Home Guard. Dad took part. He still looks very smart but he complained afterwards that they marched too slowly for a rifleman. His lot used to do 180 to the minute, which is almost running. It was an impressive sight as rank after rank marched across the huge parade ground in front of the 18th century buildings. Then they went into the Garrison Church. Dad says they prayed to God to change sides. I stayed outside and counted up the shrapnel scars from a bomb that was dropped by a Zeppelin in the Great War. Of course, I'm quite used to shrapnel scars. They are all over the place. There are also lots of neat, round holes driven deep into the pavements by firebombs. We've got four in Nesbit Road alone.

Went up to Charing Cross Road again and bought some books. I got

Southey's 'Life of Nelson' for 6d, 'Short History of Rome' by Smith, 2d, and Palgrave's 'Golden Treasury' for 1/-. Not bad. I've now got Hubert and Lang's translation of Homer which is easier reading than the Chapman version.

Can you get parachute silk down your way? My cousin Brenda had some made into underclothes. Bright yellow! Each morning I ask the girls what colour knickers they are wearing. Alma tells me in an icy voice as she walks by. Lucinda shows me!!!

Cheerio,
Bill

Machen House,
Lower Machen,
Monmouthshire.
23rd February 1941

Dear Bill,

Something terrible has happened. Charles Burton is dead. When we got to school today, everyone was talking about it. After he'd left Lady Walker's, they found a place for him at a house in Risca, which is over the mountain from us. He'd only just moved. Over the week-end the Germans bombed Swansea pretty badly. But this wasn't their only target. Risca has an aluminium factory and they went for that as well. No one seems to know exactly what happened but all we do know, is that a land-mine was dropped. I only hope to God that he was killed straight away. Some say that the house was set on fire and others say that he went back in to help rescue someone. We just don't know. Except that he's dead.

When we heard about it, the funny thing was that none of us from Machen House said a word. And none of us cried. I think we all felt like crying but I suppose we're too old for that now. All through lessons I kept thinking, why Charles? It could have been any of us. I mean, Johnny and I are always getting into fights and trouble and end up near the bottom of the class, but Charles was a quiet chap who thought of others and was really clever. Everyone liked him. Why Charles?

At the break a very strange thing happened which none of us can explain. Ronnie, Bob, Johnny and I started to fight one another. I don't know how it all began, but suddenly, the four of us were punching hell out of each other. Of course, that was the moment when Miss Pitts had to come out. Naturally, she picked on me and had me up in front of the class and really slammed into me. 'Despicable creature', 'Unfeeling', 'No respect for the dead', she just went on and on and ended up saying, 'If Mervyn is killed by a bomb then we'll all know how to behave, won't we?' Then I had the walk to Bassaleg to get myself caned by Grindle.

He read the note I'd brought and gave me two on each hand. I wanted them to hurt but they didn't. When he'd finished I just stood there with both my arms stretched out. He asked me if I wanted more. I suppose I nodded. He gave one on each hand then threw the cane on the floor. After that he looked at me for a long time, then told me to get out.

I don't know who is going to write to Gavin but I hope it's not me. I suppose Mrs Griffiths will write to the girls but it will be Grindle who has to tell his parents, poor sod. What an awful thing to have to do. And how can you forgive your enemies and turn the other cheek when something like this happens? God help any German airman who comes down near here right now. What a rotten thing this war is.

Your friend,
Merv

7, Nesbit Road,
Eltham, S.E.9.
26th February 1941

Dear Merv,

Got your letter this morning. This is a very short note to say how sorry I am for all of you.

Although Charles was in our class at Eltham, I didn't know him very well. You and I were always charging around all the time but he was such a quiet chap and kept himself to himself.

Everyone talks a lot these days about whether or not a bomb has your name on it, that it makes you think that there might be something in this business about fate.

Cheerio,
Bill

Machen House,
Lower Machen,
Monmouthshire,
15th March 1941

Dear Bill,

Today is my birthday. It's a gloomy Sunday and pouring with rain. The others have gone to church and I'm alone in the playroom. After all that has been happening recently, I didn't feel like singing in the choir—or giving thanks to God. So far, this has been an absolutely rotten year—and we're only into March.

Before I forget, thanks for your birthday card. A picture of Napoleon is much better than all those flowers and birds and things. Mum sent me one like that but no present. She said I could choose something when I went up at Easter. Probably shoes or a shirt. What I'd really like is an airgun or better still, a pistol. I won't get it because Dad has never allowed me to have warlike things. I never even had toy soldiers when I was small, because Dad said it was wrong to treat war as a game and make it seem glorious. Even though he didn't smoke,

125

he always bought matches from the blind soldier in the High Street and his paper from the paper—seller with no nose. I found a book that he'd hidden in a cupboard called 'No More War' which was full of photographs of soldiers with their faces half blown away, and bodies without any arms or legs. I think I was about eight at the time and it gave me nightmares for weeks. But I could see what Dad meant. The funny thing is, he's now working in a munitions factory.

I've gone off the track a bit. What I started off to tell you, was about last Thursday. I've made a note in my diary and called it, 'Black Thursday'. Anyway, it was raining. It's been doing a lot of that lately. When it rains we don't go outside for the break but fool around in the hall. There were four of us sitting in a circle playing whist on the floor.

Suddenly, Miss Pitts decided that the break was over, even though there was still two minutes to go and we hadn't quite finished our hand. Johnny flicked his card into the centre, which was a ten. Pitts really went mad and screamed out that the next boy who dared to throw a card was really for it. Well, as I was holding a Jack, I had to flick it, didn't I? I mean, you would have done the same wouldn't you? Besides, there was tuppence at stake. By golly, I thought the stupid bitch was going to burst a blood vessel. She stormed over, kicked the cards everywhere, then grabbed me by the collar and pulled me back to my seat. Everyone else sat down very quickly.

Then she said that for such insolent disobedience I would get six of the best and she only wished it could be more. Well, at least I'd won the tuppence, and I quickly worked out that each stroke of the cane was going to be worth a third of a penny. This thought rather pleased me and I started to smile.

Bill, that smile was my downfall! It was like a red rag to a bull—in her case, cow! I thought she was going to have a fit. It would have saved an awful lot of trouble if she had. She was screaming at the top of her voice about how evil I was and what a bad influence I was and how I should never have been allowed to come to such a decent school and simply because I was good at English it didn't excuse the fact that I was bad at everything else. She went on and on while I stood there and smiled back at her. Then she got on to Charles, how when one of my

126

so called best friends was killed, I didn't care a damn. That really hurt, so I shouted, 'Shut up you stupid bitch, you don't know what I felt'. Before I knew it, she'd picked up a ruler and slapped me across the face. She was going to do it again but I grabbed it from her and snapped it in half.

Bill, you've read about cutting the silence with a knife—well, that's what it was like. No one said a word, just Pitts breathing heavily. Then she started to laugh. No, it was more of a cackle, like one of the three witches. Really gloating. 'Haisman, ever since I joined this school I've been waiting for you to make a mistake like this. You're going to rue the day you met me!' Then she dismissed the class and went off to see Grindle.

The next morning I went straight to Bassaleg where Grindle promptly gave me three on each hand. Unfortunately by then, the mark on my face had disappeared but I could see him looking at me. Between them they had decided that my punishment was to be sent down to the bottom class with the juniors until the end of term. And we've just got two weeks revision before we do some mock exam papers—only I'll be down with the First Form, so you can imagine what my results are going to be like! I really hate that woman!

Actually, I feel a lot better now that I've got all that down on paper. Perhaps being with the juniors won't be so bad after all. At least they won't be doing logarithms and maybe I'll even understand some of the French. I expect it'll be a bit lonely though, all on my own with no one to talk to. Still, as Ronnie says, it's only for seventeen school days, then I'll be off on holiday. He's very good at working things out like that.

The girls came home at half-term and it was Heather's birthday. Someone had given her an umbrella as a present. I ask you, what sort of present is that—even for a girl! Anyway, she was as pleased as Punch and kept on putting it up and down every couple of minutes until we got fed up with the bloody thing. Then Ronnie, who as you know, fancies himself as an engineer, asked to have a look at it. He examined it very closely, then shook his head. It was no good at all and certainly wouldn't keep out the rain. So then we all looked at it and agreed that Ronnie was right. Heather got very upset and said that her umbrella was the finest that money could buy and of course it would keep out the rain. That's when Ronnie suggested it be put to the test, scientifically. No good going out in a rainstorm only to find out that it didn't work.

So, Heather agreed and stood underneath the tower holding her umbrella. We all shot up to the roof of the tower where we keep a tin bath full of water in case of firebombs. (The house might go up in flames but at least the playroom will be safe.) When she said she was ready, the four of us lifted the bath up and poured a good ten gallons of water down on her—all in one go!!! Then we raced down the stairs to see the results of Ronnie's 'scientific test'. Poor old Heather was still standing where we'd left her, but now soaked to the skin and with the remains of her umbrella draped around her. Ronnie just looked at her and said, 'There you are, I told you it wouldn't work.'

I've started to get the jitters about tomorrow again. I'll let you know how it all goes. But keep your eye on the newspapers. You may see a headline which reads, 'Boy murders school teacher.'

Your friend,

Merv

7, Nesbit Road,
Eltham, S.E.9.
21st March 1941

Dear Merv,

My word, I'm not sure who is in the greater danger, you in Wales or me up here in London. If you are planning to murder Zazu Pitts, which from the sound of it is long overdue, I would suggest you poison her. This method has been used throughout history, the Borgias having had great success. I was only caned by Grindle once and remember it well. He seems to be getting in a lot of practice on you lately. Perhaps there's a Headmasters Caning Competition coming up soon and he's gone into training. I only hope Haggar hasn't heard about it. Anyway, as Ronnie Johnson says, it's only for seventeen days and by the time you get this, you'll only have another twelve to go.

128

There was a heavy raid on London two nights ago and Eltham had its fair share of excitement. At about eight o'clock dad turned the radio off to listen out for bombers. I went to bed to get some shut-eye before the fun started. Haggar told us to do this because it would

'There was a heavy raid on London two nights' ago'

Courtesy of Hulton-Deutsch

mean we were fresh for our studies next day. Apparently he did it in the trenches during the Great War. Imagine the headlines, 'Haggar sleeps as a million Germans cross Belgium'.

Anyway, it must have been about eleven o'clock when dad woke me up. The roar of bombers and the crashing of guns was deafening. I could also hear a tinkling and clattering noise quite close outside. 'Get your clothes on', he shouted, 'the . . . (unrepeatable by a well brought up lad) . . . are dropping firebombs!' I put my clothes on over my pyjamas and we ran outside to find Nesbit Road lit up like Bonfire Night. Firebombs, which are quite small, are dropped in clusters and they seemed to be burning everywhere, so it was a job to know where to start. Two were burning very fiercely, one by our gate and the other by the school fence. We grabbed sandbags which old Rogers, the Warden, had delivered only the day before. Afterwards, dad said it was because the old devil was in close touch with Hitler.

I held the sandbag up to my face to shield my eyes and had a go at the one at the gate. As I couldn't see where I was going, my throw fell short. My next one landed right on it. The glare from these things is terrific and they melt as they burn. You need to get them out quickly because the second wave of bombers aim straight for them, so everyone in the street came out to lend a hand. After dad and I had been going for some time, I paused for a breather—and that's when I saw sparks coming from the roof of the house on the corner. Everybody seemed to have seen it at the same moment and we all rushed forward together. We were a well equipped force with buckets, stirrup pumps, sandbags and shovels to dig up earth—it would have needed a good throw to get it on to the roof though. Then some silly sod shut the front door.

Soon, from inside the house came shouts for water. It took quite a bit of loud swearing before we could make them understand they'd locked us out. While all this was going on, there was another group shouting for poles and a ladder. This was because one bomb was jammed in the guttering. When someone did manage to find a ladder, there was a lot of pushing and pulling as they tried to get it up. One man fell through the fence and another put his elbow through a window and Rogers was shouting orders all the time. Dad said it was like something out of Fred Karno's Army. Eventually they got the ladder up and the bomb was hooked out of the guttering, but by now the roof was burning. We really needed the Fire Brigade but you could see they were busy in other parts of Eltham because there was a fierce glow in the sky from the direction of the High Street. Still, we did finally put the fire out, although most of the roof has gone.

While we were busy fire fighting, there were bombs dropping, guns crashing and shrapnel clattering all around. It's funny, but somehow you never expect to get hit by these red hot jagged pieces of metal. It only comes home to you when you see someone who has been hit. I saw one man being led away to the First Aid Centre. There was a gash down one side of his face that was pouring blood. We wear tin hats but dad says they'd never stop shrapnel. The guns on the common kick up one hell of a row when the bombers are in range. The trouble is, they never seem to hit anything.

As dad and I walked back along the road we found another bomb spluttering. I grabbed a shovel, dug up some earth and threw it on the thing. Dad said I looked like a devil stoking the fires of Hell. By then it was two a.m. and the whole sky was alight. London was really burning. A warden ran by and asked if 'our' bomb was out. We couldn't see anything burning in the road so we said yes. When we walked round the back of our house we realised what he was talking about. Mum's clothes post was a charred wreck!! Dad swore a lot because he'll have to buy a new one—but it will be me who'll have to fix it. Dad always says he'll help but at the last moment he'll find something else to do that's far more important—like going on parade with the Home Guard. I think most of his parading takes place in the saloon bar of the 'Greyhound'. I hate fixing up the clothes post. This will be the third one. The first one broke under the weight of washing and the second one came down in a gale—and each time I was the one who got the blame. I expect I'll be blamed for this bloody firebomb as well.

Next morning at Assembly we all had firebomb stories to swap. As he was late turning up, it was generally agreed that Haggar probably

7 Nesbit Road. The road is named after E. Nesbit, author of *The Railway Children*, who lived in Eltham. The firebombs fell where the car *(left)* is standing in this 1990 photograph

slept through the lot. Two boys have lost their homes. According to Alma, she seems to have saved several thousand from burning to death and my humble story of the 'Great Clothes Post' raid went down well. Then Haggar strode into the hall and told us all to get down on the floor. This unusual order got us all giggling until he told us that a bomb disposal squad were about to deal with two unexploded bombs that had fallen during the night. We were hardly sprawled out on the floor when two tremendous crashes rocked the school, bringing dust and plaster down all over us. Some of the girls screamed so several of the lads took the opportunity to give them a cuddle. I gave Lucinda a cuddle even though she hadn't screamed. Luckily, while all this was going on, Haggar was busy dusting off his pre-historic suit. Did I tell you, he still wears a butterfly collar? The bombs were quite near, in Sherard Road.

Haggar decided recently that we needed a school reporter to write about the school for the local rag. Miss Wilcox, being a clever woman, recommended me. Haggard scowled like mad but agreed. My first report burbled on about pupils working in ideal conditions in modern buildings set in spacious grounds, about the wide range of subjects we study, and the dedicated band of teachers working under the guidance of Haggar—I'm no fool, Merv. I also somehow managed to get in a mention of a sports day when I had won the 220 yards. Haggar sent for me and said that he liked the report but he was puzzled by the fact that only one winner was mentioned. I said it was due to lack of space. For the first time he actually smiled at me.

Cheerio,
Bill

Machen House,
Lower Machen,
Monmouthshire.
8th April 1941

Dear Bill,

Your firebomb raid sounded really exciting and in spite of all the bombs and death and destruction, I wish I was back in Eltham. I didn't realise what a terrible punishment being banished to the First Form was going to be. Having the cane is one thing—even six of the best. It might hurt like hell at the time but at least it's over and done with. This went on for nearly a month!!! There was no pain outside, but inside I hurt a lot and I felt like crying but I knew I didn't dare. I just had to pretend that I didn't care, but of course, I did.

The first shock I had was the size of the desks. I expect you've grown as much as I have but it's something you don't realise. I could hardly fit into a First Form desk and this made the class laugh—until I turned round and glared at them. The work itself was so easy that I finished it in half the time. I was so bored with nothing to do, that after a couple of days I went to Grindle and asked if I could be given revision work for the end of term exams. The silly little bugger gave that thin smile of his and said, 'That is not the purpose of this exercise.' I wasn't even allowed to go on to the next lesson. All I could do was sit there, twiddle my thumbs and think up terrible ways of torturing Miss Pitts.

I think the worst times were the breaks and dinner hour. I never knew they could last so long. In the class, at least I had something to do, but in the breaks there was nothing. I couldn't join in their stupid games, and of course, there was no one to talk to, so I ended up standing in a corner of the playground on my own. I used to think that being 'Sent to Coventry' wasn't much of a punishment, but now I know different. After a week, I asked Mrs Evans if I could borrow her Daily Mirror to take to school. By the time I returned it to her in the afternoon, I would have read every single word. I don't know if your Dad takes the Mirror, but if he does, you'll find that Cassandra is worth reading and Jane is worth looking at.

When it came to the exams I was top in English and in Art. I did a picture of our church, complete with yew trees and big storm clouds piling up behind. I called it, 'The Approaching Storm'. It was done in charcoal and looked quite dramatic. In all the other subjects I ended up near the bottom—except French, where I was bottom. The others reckoned I hadn't done too badly and now that the punishment was over, I'd be able to start fresh next term.

Somehow I knew it would never be the same again. Of course we were still friends but during this last month something had changed. Difficult to explain, but it was though I wasn't part of them anymore. Perhaps it was because in class they'd moved on and I was left behind. I'd worked out how I was going to have my revenge on Pitts. It wasn't much of a revenge but it was the best I could think of. I'd cycled all the way into Newport and for 6d bought a small packet of itching powder. I even took the precaution of wearing my mac over the school uniform and wore my glasses so that I couldn't be recognised. And I didn't tell anyone what I was going to do—not even Ronnie.

On the last day of term, during the dinner break, I told everyone I was going to the bog, then slipped back into school. I poured the powder into a horrible knitted hat that Pitts always wears, knowing that she wouldn't put it on until after we'd all gone home. Or so I thought! Unfortunately it started to rain and soon it was chucking it down. That's when Pitts came out to call us all in—wearing her hat!

As soon as we started the lesson Pitts began to scratch. Not much at first, but then more and more and more. That's when the class started to laugh at her. Not me, I didn't dare. Soon, everyone was falling about watching her claw at her head. I was a fool Bill, I should have laughed. I stood out like a sore thumb—and the bitch spotted this. Before long I was standing in front of Grindle once again. I'll tell you this, there's no such thing as justice. There wasn't a shred of evidence to say that I had done the deed. Except the fact that I didn't laugh at her. What sort of evidence is that?!! I told him I had severe tooth-ache at the time, which I felt was a pretty reasonable excuse for not laughing. The disbelieving sod called me a liar.

During all this Pitts was still scratching her head like mad and there were hair combs and clips all over the floor. She really did look a sight, her hair all tangled up and practically foaming with rage. Finally she screamed at him, 'Headmaster, either that boy goes or I do.' There was a long pause as Grindle thought about this. By now, some of the powder had got down her back, so besides scratching her head, she was also jiggling around like a dancing Dervish. When Grindle said, 'Miss Pitts, why don't you go and put your head under a tap', I thought that I had won and all that going to church had paid off. Alas, no.

When we were alone, he said he would give me an option. If I chose not to come back from my holiday in North Wales he would understand that the family bond had proved to be stronger than the ties of school. If however, I did return, the very first thing he would do next term, would be to expel me!!!! What sort of option is that?

What the hell am I going to tell Mum and Dad? I'm meant to be going up there for a holiday, not for good. And yet I'll be arriving with everything I own in the world. I'll have to come up with a pretty good story. I can't tell them that I've been expelled because they were so pleased that I managed to get into the school and to buy my uniform they had to go without. I suppose I'll think of something.

Of course, this means that I'll never see Gavin or Bridget again. I don't even know where they live. I had thought of leaving a letter behind for Bridget telling her that I loved her, but if I'm not going to see her again there doesn't seem much point.

I understand from Mrs Griffiths that Gavin took Charles's death pretty badly. I wonder if he'll want to come back to Machen House. I shall miss this place and all my friends, but it would have had to come to an end one day anyway.

My address in North Wales will be: 27, Tudor Drive, Llandudno Junction, Caernarvonshire. Will write to you once I've settled in, so don't expect a letter straight away.

Your friend,
Merv

7, Nesbit Road,
Eltham, S.E.9.
20th April 1941
(Hitler's birthday)

Dear Merv,

You poor old chum, you really have been going through it haven't you? And what a swine Grindle has turned out to be. I thought Haggar was bad enough, but he wouldn't do a thing like that—even to me. As for the Zazu creature, all I can say, is that you're well rid of her. It will probably turn out that she's either a member of the Gestapo or a Fifth Columnist. As this is the first time I've written to you in North Wales, please let me know if your letters are read. I don't expect they are, but I thought I'd better check. Of course, I won't breathe a word at this end about what you've told me, because if the girls got hold of it the whole world would know within forty-eight hours.

Here's some good news to cheer you up. I've sold three of your silver paper pictures for 10/-. I had to get cracking as they were going mouldy in my room. Two Donald Ducks and one Sleepy. He's the one of the Seven Dwarfs who most reminds me of old Spotty Prince. In looks, that is. Spotty is certainly not sleepy the way he jumps about, yelling and shouting at us. We lost a pencil during Technical Drawing. 'Nobody leaves until the pencil is found', he bawled. We wandered around for a bit, pretending to look for it, then Roberts took a pencil out of the box when he wasn't looking and handed it to him. 'There you are', cried Spotty in triumph, 'It was lost and is found!' We all shot out of the class before he started counting them again.

But enough of these larks. I promised to send you war reports from the front line, so here is the latest. A few nights ago we had a really big raid. Somehow you knew it was going to be big. About nine o'clock the sirens began going near and far, seeming to take up the cry from each other. A weird, strange noise really. Of course, by now I've got together a collection of clothes for night raids; two jerseys, a jerkin, a long green scarf, a tin helmet, a gas mask, and to go over the lot of

Courtesy of London Transport Museum

'A really big raid'. Plumstead Road, Woolwich, 19th April 1940. The men in the background are pulling down a dangerous roof

137

all this—a mack. It's surprising how cold it gets in the early hours of the morning—something I never knew about before the war. There were the usual droning engines, waving searchlights, gunfire, flares, and then—unusual this—machine gun fire. So, dad and I went out into the garden. Suddenly there was a scream which grew louder every second. This was going to be a close one we thought, as we threw ourselves down. Yes, I do remember what your brother, Eric says, but I prefer to be safe than sorry. The crash was terrific. It rocked the ground and we could hear crockery tinkling as things were smashed inside the house, so we ran in to make sure that mum was all right. When we came out again, there was a huge fire going which seemed to be right behind the school caretaker's house opposite. Of course, it was not as near as that but up at Kidbrooke. We could hear the crackle of bullets exploding.

Dad worked out that the ammunition dump beside the station was the target and that it had been hit earlier by a firebomb hence the 'machine gun' fire we'd heard. It was the second bomb that really got things going. The sky was all colours, orange and blue and green with showers of bright sparks shooting up through the clouds of black smoke. The noise was tremendous with bangs, cracks and sudden whooshes as Very lights shot up like rockets. We wanted to cycle up the lane for a better view but dad had been told to guard the street, so we had to stay put to watch this grand firework display. It went on for over an hour. Afterwards, mum made us oxo and and we had dripping on toast. Very tasty!

Next morning mum came back from the High Street with a piece of coconut matting for the kitchen. She said that on the way home at least half a dozen people had stopped her to ask where she'd got it and had they anymore in. One woman handed over her pram to her husband, ran like mad and jumped on a tram that was going quite fast. We all wondered if she'd got there before they'd sold out.

While mum had been queuing, she'd heard that the buildings in Avery Hill Park had been burnt out by firebombs in the night, so I got on my bike and went over to see for myself. When I got there, parts of the buildings were still burning and there was a wreath of smoke round the ivy-clad tower. Tired and dirty firemen were still dousing the ruins.

The roar of the five tenders they were using to pump water was terrific. They had five hoses going across the road but it was easy to get over them because they'd placed planks either side. This didn't stop a couple of coppers taking charge and sending all the traffic on a three mile detour. Three miles for five hose pipes! Ye Gods, war does bring out the daftness in mankind! Especially coppers! How many times have they told me to move on and not form a crowd when I was the only one there!!!

This was a very heavy raid according to the news bulletins. You might read about it on the stone tablets which pass for newspapers in wild Wales. St. Pauls has been hit and is, apparently, badly damaged. Trafalgar Square and the centre of London has taken a severe bashing again. Worse still, from dad's point of view, the dance hall at the Yorkshire Grey has got an unexploded bomb buried underneath it. The very next day after this happened, dad's Home Guard platoon moved their H.Q. to The Greyhound—a striking example of their adaptability, dad claims. God help the Germans if they ever land and attack a pub!

Now for the really important news. Alma has been made a prefect. A few days before the end of term she and Lucinda had an awful row. No one seems to know what it was about but Lucinda slapped Alma's face and they both ended up crying their eyes out. Haggar appeared and talked to them like a Dutch uncle, which made them cry even more. Mrs Boon was less sympathetic; she wanted them caned!! For a while we all thought history was about to be made. I ask you, a girl caned! The lads were all taking bets as to exactly where they would be caned, but it all fell through and they got 500 lines instead. Lucinda got, 'Young ladies do not slap other young ladies faces'. Alma got, 'Young ladies do not get their faces' slapped' I can't quite see the sense in that, can you? Anyway, Alma was furious. She doesn't think prefects should have to write lines. Still, it might make her think twice before she dishes them out to some of the younger girls in future. I told her she ought to thank her lucky stars she hadn't been caned but

139

it turned out her few lines had cost her a lot. Her parents were so upset by her bad behaviour that they stopped her pocket money for two weeks. When she told me I couldn't stop laughing, which didn't help at all.

My performance in 'School for Scandal' was as good as MY press report could make it. In fact, I forgot some of my lines. Lucinda helped me out by whispering them to me. I was surprised because she seemed to know my lines better than her own. The audience of mums and dads clapped like mad. We've been asked to give another public performance at the Progress Hall. As it's owned by the Co-op, dad says we ought to call ourselves the 'Dividend Players'.

I'm enclosing a P.O. for 8/- for your silver paper pictures. (10/- less my commission of 20%.) I've only got one left which is a Mickey Mouse. No one seems to like it but I'll do my best. It's taken me nearly a year to sell the lot you sent up from Deal, so I hope you've stopped making them. If you haven't, and have been building up a secret stockpile, then I suggest you try selling them to the Welsh—although I doubt that they've even heard of Mickey Mouse up there.

By the way, how are your 'high wild hills and rough uneven ways'? (Shakespeare—Richard III—our set book for the Oxford.) Write soon.

> Cheerio,
> Bill

> 27, Tudor Drive,
> Llandudno Junction,
> Caernarvonshire.
> 8th May 1941

Dear Bill,

Your letter arrived safely and wasn't read. Of course, Mum guessed it was from you and wanted to know how you were getting on, so I gave her all the latest news from Eltham. She was quite upset about Avery Hill because when I was small, she often used to take me up there in my pushchair. She has a photograph of me standing under one of the huge oak trees when I was two. I look like a dwarf. I used to love being taken into the big glass hothouse and seeing all the palm trees and tropical fish. I suppose that's just a pile of rubble now.

Anyway, you'll want to know what has been happening since I last wrote to you. Everything was very different from what I'd expected, because when the time came for me to leave Machen House, I didn't mind at all. Here was I going off on a new adventure while all the others were going to stay behind doing the same old things. Ronnie said he felt really sad, and I think he meant it because we'd been together ever since the Infants at Ealdham Square. Of course, all the Griffiths knew I wouldn't be coming back and the reason why. The Colonel had a few words with me and said in that funny way of his, 'Hear you've been in a bit of a scrape, lad. Often happens. Helps form character, what? Eh? Eh?' Then he gave me sixpence, slapped me on the shoulder and walked off. By the time I'd finished packing my suitcase it was bulging and very heavy, so the others helped me down to the bus stop with it. Just as well I was wearing my raincoat because it started to rain. I told them to push off back to the house and as I watched them go I suddenly felt very grown up.

A very funny thing happened at Newport station. I'd just got off the bus and was wondering where to go, when I heard a voice say, 'Boy, put your cap on.' I turned around and there was Grindle, who obviously hadn't recognised me. As soon as he saw who I was, he went quite red and mumbled, 'Ah, Haisman...yes...Well, have a safe journey.' Then he legged it. I wish I'd been fast enough to say something really witty. Even 'bollocks' would have been better than just staring at him.

Somewhere between Hereford and Shrewsbury I heard the air raid warning. So did the driver because he kept the train stuck in a tunnel for thirty minutes. I had to change at Chester and with all the station signs taken down it was very difficult to work out exactly where you were. I had an hour to wait at Chester so I put my case in the Left Luggage and walked around the town. Lots of Tudor buildings and in one street they had shops on the ground and another level of shops above them. I've never seen anything like that before. When I finally got here, Mum was waiting for me at the station. Luckily she didn't cry, but got pretty near to it.

The house where we live was only built in 1936 so it's very modern. We have the sitting room at the front and a bedroom. Mum has to share the kitchen with Mrs Lloyd and they don't get on well together at all. And whenever we want a bath, we have to tell her the day before so that she can light the boiler. There's only enough water for two baths, so Mum has hers first, then Dad. Once the water's heated up again, Vevlie has her bath and I use her water. Mum gets really cross about this as she says hot water was included in the rent. At home there's no problem because the only time we can have a bath is on Sunday when the fire in the front room is lit.

Dad is on permanent night work, which is just as well. Mum and Vev sleep together in the double bed at night and Dad uses it during the day. I sleep on the settee downstairs. By God, can Dad snore! When he really gets going, his snores rattle the brass ornaments on the mantlepiece. He says it's taken a lifetime of training. Before the war he used to drop off to sleep on the couch in the kitchen when he got home from work. When he started to snore everyone would shout, 'DAD!' and he'd wake up and claim he wasn't snoring. He had a habit of falling asleep with his hand stretched out, and sometimes Vev would walk past and put an apple in it, which really annoyed him.

The Lloyds, who own the house, aren't at all friendly. Vev says that they resent the fact that they've had to let off rooms, which no one else in the street does. The woman is small, doesn't smile and never stops cleaning. Every time we come in, she goes up and down the hall with her carpet cleaner. I don't know if the husband is dumb but I've never heard him say a word. Not that he gets a chance because she never stops. Even when you meet him, all you get is a nod. He wears thick, pebble glasses and so does the son, Robert. When the two of them are together, it's like looking at frog spawn.

Dad only gets Sunday off and last week the two of us went off on our own. I can't tell you exactly where we ended up because most of the names up here are impossible anyway, but it was a huge reservoir way up in the mountains—and underneath all that water was a village!

Mervyn and his mother with the Lloyd family

They just built a dam and flooded the whole valley. Dad said that sometimes you can still hear the church bell ringing, way down under the water. I reckon he was pulling my leg. He's a great one for jokes and he's got the cheek of the devil. Once, he found a brooch on the pavement outside Hinds the jewellers, in Lewisham, so he took it home and gave it to Vev. She liked it very much but found that the clasp was broken. Dad got very annoyed, went straight back to Lewisham, marched into Hinds and demanded that they mended it on the spot—without charge. And he got away with it. How's that for cheek?

There are some good beaches around here at Llandudno and Colwyn Bay so when it gets warmer I'll be able to practice my swimming. It looks as though I'm going to have a lot of time to do this. They don't have Central schools up here so Mum went along to the local Grammar school to get me enrolled. They said they'd be very happy to have me provided I could speak Welsh!!! I can't even speak French so what chance have I got with a language that has words like: Llanfairpwllgwyngyllgogerychwyrndrobwllllandysiliogogogoch???

Just in case you're a bit slow in working it out, it means, 'St.Mary's church in the hollow of the white hazel near to the rapid whirlpool of St.Tysillio's church by the red cave.' Why couldn't they just say, St.Mary's church? I mean, just how many St.Mary's churches have they got in that part of the world? The place must be splattered with them!!

As you can guess, I am not going to even attempt to learn Welsh. Which means no school. Vev has said she's willing to set me lessons every night, which is fine for geography and French—she's good at that unfortunately, but when it comes to things like logarithms, I probably know more than she does—which is next to nothing. Dad feels that this is the ideal opportunity for me to take up painting and weight lifting. A creative mind and a strong body is all any man needs he reckons. He says that a really intelligent man is someone who can be shipwrecked on a desert island and survive. I think that if he were really intelligent, he wouldn't have got himself shipwrecked in the first place.

144

Up here, you wouldn't know there was a war on, except that for the last few nights there have been air raids on Liverpool. This is miles and miles from here and you could only just hear the gunfire and bombs and see a red glow in the sky. To hear Mrs Lloyd talk you'd think the Blitz was on her doorstep. She was even thinking of going to stay with her sister somewhere up in the mountains. Mum quite liked this idea but nothing has come of it so far.

Eric would have been very annoyed if the Yorkshire Grey Ballroom had been blown up, because every year this is where Middle Park Football Club hold their annual dance. I don't know if I told you, but Eric started the club in 1928. It was when he was on the dole during the Slump. None of the team had any money for jerseys or boots, so Eric went up to Eltham Palace, where a millionaire lived called Courtauld, and asked him for the money. He gave it to them and so he became the Club's first President. At the moment, Jimmy Seed of Charlton is the President. Anyway, each year Eric makes everyone hire evening dress for the annual dance. Fred Routledge, his friend, always grumbles and kicks up a hell of a fuss about this. But Eric is a great stickler for getting things right and it's a very posh affair with a dance band and a proper dinner. I wonder if Fred Routledge tipped off the Germans that the Yorkshire Grey was a vital target? That would be the only way to win an argument with Eric.

You'll be pleased to hear that I have no more silver paper pictures. I'd run out of glass anyway, but I did bring the silver paper with me because you can't get it now. I don't know how I can use it but it's too valuable to throw away. The one thing I did leave behind was my bike. By the time I left, the front wheel was buckled, the brake cable had snapped and the saddle had a nasty habit of tipping backwards when you didn't expect it. The only thing that worked was the bell and that was pretty rusty. I expect it will end up as scrap for the war effort.

Well, that's about all the news from here at the moment. I had wondered whether I might get a letter from the lads at Machen House or Joan Longley. They all have my address. Not a word. Sod the lot of them. I expect that's just how Livingstone felt in the middle of Africa. Write soon.   Your friend, Merv

7, Nesbit Road,
Eltham, S.E.9.
13th May 1941

Dear Merv,

Very interesting about your brother Eric and Middle Park Football Club. I hope he wasn't planning another dance, because the bomb under the 'Yorkshire Grey' went up last week and has completely wrecked the ballroom. The pub is in a bit of a state as well. Dad says it was wise of the Home Guard to move to the 'Greyhound', which they all agree is a better H.Q. They talk about 'better fields of fire', but I think they prefer the beer.

A few nights ago London had a very heavy raid. A bomb hit the Houses of Parliament. Nobody was killed because it was during the night. Dad said the Germans had carried on where Guy Fawkes left off. He always claims Guy Fawkes was the only man to go into the House of Commons with a sensible idea in his head. When I pointed out that Guy Fawkes never actually went into the House of Commons, dad told me not to spoil a good joke with the truth.

Over at Catford the wreckage is incredible. The shops near the Town Hall are so badly damaged it is impossible to work out what sort of shops they were. In Westhorne Avenue, a bomb has turned a house into a deep hole with rubble piled ten feet high round it. The whole pavement has moved forward about two feet. It's obvious they are using bigger bombs. Some of this I sleep through and other times I am up and about. Mum is as well as can be expected but she worries a lot, especially when dad and I are away at work or school. Actually it's strange how you get used to it. We were talking about this only the other day. The siren went and we all picked up our things and went out to the shelter—quite automatically—as though we'd been doing it all our lives. It got me thinking. I mean, imagine all this going on before the war! We wouldn't have believed it, would we? My biggest problem then was glandular fever. Now I feel I'm lucky to have a body to have glandular fever in.

The other afternoon I found a chalk drawing on the top of my desk lid. It was either meant to be Miss Wilcox or the Witch in Snow White.

146

I just sat down and looked at it. After all, Wilcox is no fool. She knows I wouldn't draw on my own desk, particularly as Haggar gave a real thrashing to a lad who carved his name on a table in the Science Lab. Just as Wilcox opened the door, Alma (who'd drawn it), got cold feet and rushed across to rub it out, knocking over my inkwell as she did so. Wilcox gave her 200 lines for being out of her place—she likes everyone in their place when she enters—300 lines for knocking over the inkwell and, biggest joke of all, 500 lines for cuddling a boy. She'd fallen into my lap, you see, as she tried to get away. Miss Wilcox does this sort of thing, (lines I mean, not cuddling boys!). She dishes out lines like a Judge handing out years in prison. She tells you exactly what each line is for. Still, she doesn't report you to Haggar because she doesn't believe in caning. She says it's because she's a Socialist, though I don't know what that's got to do with it. Actually, she's against the war and won't let us collect money for 'Spitfire Weeks' and things like that, in her lessons. She's the best teacher we've got though, and is marvellous at English. Well, she must be because she's always praising my essays.

Going back to Alma, she's having a rough time lately. This latest bit of trouble means she is no longer a prefect; you can only be punished twice and then you lose your badge. Haggar announced it in Assembly in a voice of doom and with a face like Boris Karloff in a Frankenstein movie. Poor Alma's face was the colour of beetroot; she's a bit ruddy at the best of times. Now she's no longer a prefect, the other girls are all giving her hell and there's nothing she can do about it. I offered to write some of her lines and she swore at me! I've never heard a girl swear before, have you? It wasn't that bad a word, but it did give me the chance to tell her she wasn't a lady. She promptly burst into tears and said that I wasn't a gentleman or I would have rubbed the drawing out and she only did it because she knew I was fond of Miss Wilcox. And I was supposed to know all this? I ask you! Women!!!

Lucinda has changed her hair. She gave everyone a surprise when she came to school with her hair down her back nearly to the waist. It looks jolly nice. She said she got fed up with piling it all on top for Lady Teazle. Which reminds me. The show at the Co-Op hall went

147

very well until somebody threw a brick through a window. Nobody could find out who did it but I suspect Coppernob, the Elementary school scruff. He hates us doing plays and calls me a sissy for liking acting. I've had a go at him twice. The first time I got a nose bleed, but the second time I managed to knock one of his teeth out. My poor dear grandfather would have been proud of me.

Last week, as part of a war effort drive to raise money, we sold ice cream in the High Street. It had been made by the girls and tasted lousy. Still, what can you expect with hardly any milk or sugar? We

'A few nights ago London had a very heavy raid'

Courtesy of Imperial War Museum

lost our last football match of the season against a team of Army Cadets. The game was interrupted twice by soldiers who were blowing up bombs in the next field. They would walk over, tell us to take cover, and then the crash would send showers of mud and rubbish over us. The cadets are boy-soldiers at the Woolwich barracks. I told dad I wouldn't mind being a boy-soldier. He said forget it.

Dad went to the Somme when he was only sixteen and it seems to have put him off. In any case, in this war the army want to see birth certificates. In the Great War they were so short of men they took anybody, providing they could see and had two arms and two legs. Dad ran away from home and joined the Royal West Kents at Canterbury. My grandfather found out, went down there and brought him back. So dad ran away again! This time he reached Cowley Barracks at Oxford which was the depot for the Ox and Bucks Light Infantry. As this was a Rifle Regiment he was able to transfer to the Rifle Brigade. This was grandfather's old regiment and so he let dad stay in the army. Clever. Dad was actually trained by men who had known grandfather.

Did I ever tell you that my grandfather tried to write his life with a John Bull printing set? It took him about two weeks to do one page! Where that one page has gone to now that he's dead, I just don't know. His medals seem to have disappeared as well. Dad didn't want them. Funny that.

Cheerio,
Bill

P.S.   One of your Donald Ducks has come back. Well, nearly. The boy asked for his money. I told him to clear off. We had a fight and he saw reason. The things I do for you!

Bill's father, 1917—he joined up at 15

27, Tudor Drive,
Llandudno Junction,
Caernarvonshire.
8th June 1941

Dear Bill,

Thanks for your news about the Yorkshire Grey. I don't suppose
Eric will be that upset, because Middle Park Football Club won't be
playing again until the war is over. I don't know if Epps is still the
landlord, but if he is, I hope that rotten dog of his got killed when the
bomb went off. As you know, the Yorkshire Grey is surrounded by
concrete which makes it a smashing place for skating. I suppose I was
about ten when it happened. I was skating away, not doing anyone any
harm, when this bloody dog of Epps' charges out of a side gate and
bites me on the hip. Of course Mum took me around to the doctor's
right away. He was out, so his wife poured a whole bottle of iodine
into the wound. By golly, did I yell! It's made me scared of dogs ever
since.

I thought that not going to school and having all that time on my
hands, meant that I'd be bored. But I was wrong. You wouldn't believe
the amount of reading I've been doing. I have a regular routine. Soon
as I've had breakfast, I walk to Conway Library. It's a fair walk, over
the bridge and past the old castle—no, I don't know who built it.
Probably Norman. I allow myself fifteen minutes to choose a book, then
it's back home. By ten-thirty I'm busy reading. Generally, I can get
through an average size book in a day.

To begin with, Dad and Vev suggested books they thought I ought
to read, but I've mixed up their list with anything that takes my fancy.
I'm quite sure your Miss Wilcox wouldn't approve at all. To give you
some idea, I can go from one of the Saint books to Joseph Conrad, on
to Dornford Yates, back to Sinclair Lewis, Jack London and Conan
Doyle. Then it might be Wells, Maugham and Macaulay—or even
modern verse. I've just read 'A Dream in the Luxembourg' and 'The
White Cliffs'. Not bad. Vev said I should read Jane Eyre, which was
long and dreary and Dad found me two secondhand books, Slocum's

Sailing Alone Around the World, which was great and Fields, Factories and Workshops. Ten pages and I gave up.

As for the weight lifting, we couldn't find any weights so Dad has taught me something called dynamic tension. You just have to imagine the weights that you lift or pull. I know it must sound a bit daft but it really does work. When he was young, Dad did both weight lifting and Ju-jitsu. He once fought the world champion at Chatham Empire, a Jap called Yoka Tani. Of course Dad didn't win but he was the best challenger of the week. He's shown me a couple of throws. A pity you're not up here. We also do a bit of boxing now and then which Mum doesn't like. Dad's still very strong and he can lift me above his head with one hand. Mum doesn't like him doing that either. Reckons he only does it to show off, then Vevlie has to chip in and tell him that he's asking for a rupture. Women are very funny. I mean, if we weren't strong, how could we protect them?

A very strange thing happened the other day. We were on the beach, and as I came back from a swim I could see that Mum had been crying, so I asked her what was wrong. She said she was just being silly and she wasn't sad at all. She was so happy that my legs were straight. I wasn't quite sure how to answer that one, so I simply nodded and sat down. Then it all came out. Apparently, when I was very small I had rickets and was knock-kneed. Something I never knew. Mum used to take me twice a week to a German woman who had a clinic in Woolwich and she made me do special exercises to get the legs straight again. Strange really. I've spent so much time cursing the Huns, yet I owe the fact that my legs are straight to a German. Perhaps she was really Austrian.

There's a very funny story going around up here about clothes rationing. As you know, they're using the margarine coupons for this, and as Vev works in the Ministry of Food, she got to hear about it. Apparently, Churchill didn't want clothes rationed at all, but Oliver Lyttleton told him it was necessary. Finally Churchill agreed but wasn't sure exactly what the ration should be, so he asked Lyttleton what he thought the average man in the street needed. Lyttleton said

Mervyn, aged 1 year 10 months. The rickets showing clearly in the left leg

he wasn't sure either, but if it was any help, he himself had forty-two suits!!! No wonder he wasn't worried about clothes rationing!

Now that Mum and I are alone a lot, we've had quite a few chats. This is something we never did before, but I suppose that was because I was younger. Now she treats me almost like a grown-up. She's told me a lot of what happened when she was young and she says that my wanting to go on the stage probably comes from her side of the family. She used to do a lot of acting and singing then but gave it up when she got married. At Rochester, she was once in a play with Sybil Thorndyke, who came from that part of the world. Mum and her brother Frank, were always singing in concerts together. She said that Uncle Frank's voice was better than Nelson Eddy's and His Master's Voice even offered him a contract, but he turned it down. He went on to be a Stage Director with Gerald Du Maurier, Cochran and Jack Buchanan, which is quite something.

Her older brother Victor—well, her step-brother really—is quite a big-wig with the BBC in Manchester. She said that one day when he was listening to 2LO, he turned to his father and told him that he could do better than that. Grandad said it was no good telling him, go up to London and tell them! So he did. Walked all the way from Rochester. They gave him an audition and the next week he was Uncle Victor on Children's Hour. After that he used to give commentaries on the TT races each year, and now he's wired up a lot of the music halls up north. For this, he sits in a box at the theatre, in full evening dress, and tells the listeners what's happening. I don't know how he manages when they have jugglers on the bill. Their family name was Smith, but this wasn't grand enough for the theatre, so they changed it to Smythe. I can't remember meeting either of them but Mum says I have. Anyway, listen out for Victor Smythe.

Vevlie is working so hard, she even does it while she's asleep. It's true. Mum said that the other night, Vev suddenly sat bolt upright in bed and started typing on Mum's back. And the night before that, she really gave everyone a scare. It was about two in the morning when Vev gave out a loud scream. I rushed up to the bedroom and the Lloyds came out on to the landing wanting to know what was going on.

Frank Smythe

Victor Smythe

Apparently, Vev woke up and saw this 'white thing' by the side of the bed, floating in mid-air. Slowly it started to move from side to side, and then finally, it rose up, rushed towards her and hit her straight in the face. Of course, what really happened, was that she'd gone to sleep on her arm and her hand had gone dead. We had a good laugh about it, but the Lloyds couldn't see the funny side of it at all. Still, what can you expect from people who go to chapel twice on Sunday. They certainly don't approve of us heathens.

Your friend,

Merv

7, Nesbit Road,
Eltham, S.E.9.
3rd July 1941

Dear Merv,

Well, we certainly live in exciting times, what with your sister's hands flying about in the middle of the night and Hitler attacking Russia. How about that? Dad is very surprised that Churchill has agreed to help Russia. He said that such a hater of Communism must be pretty desperate to make friends with someone like Stalin. After all, he did his best after the Great War to see that the Russian Revolution failed. This latest attack makes our chances of winning the war much better now that they are fighting on another front. On the other hand, the Russians did so badly against the Finns I wonder if they'll be able to hold out against the Germans? At least we may have a bit less bombing now.

At school, Miss Wilcox was delighted by the news. This is because she is a Communist. She told me that actually she was a Marxist. And there was I thinking she was a Socialist. Dad explained that a Marxist is a sort of Communist with brains. Haggar is not at all happy with the news. I think he is a Conservative or a National Liberal, which dad says is the same thing. Anyway, he goes into the Conservative Club at the top of the High Street—I've seen him. Of course, this may simply mean that he prefers snooker to billards. Dad says that billiards is the poor man's game. They play it over Montagu Burton. Snooker is played with lots of coloured balls and is very popular in Tory clubs. So, Haggar is probably a snooker-playing Conservative. Personally, I think he's a lunatic, Grade One.

Here in Eltham all sorts of things are in short supply. Things you wouldn't expect. I went into Malins the other day to get a birthday card for my granny. Old man Malin put on a long face and said they hadn't got any and then went into a long story of how he couldn't get cards from someone called Meredith and it was all to do with the shortage of cardboard and coloured ink and when he did manage to get a few, the quality wasn't the same as before the war. He went on for so long that I wished I hadn't asked.

Miss Wilcox suggested we had a school magazine, so there was a vote for editor. Roberts got 4 votes, Smithson 1 and I got 23. Haggar wasn't at all happy but he knows Miss Wilcox is a first class teacher who can keep order without a cane. I've written a play for the next school concert called 'Vice and Virtue'. It's a morality play and guess who's going to be Virtue? Miss Wilcox wants this play put in the magazine, plus an essay I wrote about Napoleon, plus my editorial. That makes a total of 14 pages. Naturally I'm not very popular. I told them it was all Miss Wilcox's idea but no one believed me. Of course, no sooner was the school magazine idea suggested than the girls began to write poems. Within a day, Alma rushed up with a sloppy poem about trees. Lucinda wrote a lovely one about her cat. I thought it best to agree to publish both. After all, I didn't want to start another round of face-slapping, did I?

Both Lucinda and Alma are now prefects; Alma has been forgiven by Haggar, probably because she flickered her big eyes at him. They are both playing at being ladies these days and are being awfully polite to one another. Funny, when you know that they really want to scratch each others' eyes out.

You mentioned clothing coupons in your last letter—well we certainly know all about them at this end. A few days ago, some fool started throwing a plimsoll around in class. All the boys took a hand and soon it was really flying, bouncing off desks, smashing into glass cases and missing people by inches. Then the girls came in from cookery and sat down with very disapproving looks. All of a sudden the plimsoll took a standing inkwell off a desk and sprayed ink all over Elsie Taylor. It was quite an amazing sight. She had on the green gingham dress that our girls wear in the summer, and it was sprayed from top to bottom. She jumped up and started screaming her head off because it was all over her face and hair as well. That was when Miss Wilcox came in!!

As I've told you, Miss Wilcox normally keeps things away from Haggar, but this time what could she do? I haven't studied this clothes rationing system too carefully, but the girls have—particularly Elsie Taylor—who said that her dress amounted to 11 coupons. Anyway, within the twinkling of an eye, Haggar had got Mr Taylor up to the school; I think he must have been hiding in the bushes outside waiting for someone to throw ink all over his lovely daughter. We knew we were in for it, but Taylor turned out to be a real sport. He burbled on about having been a boy himself once, etc, etc. BUT the dress had cost 11/6, it was brand new, and what about the coupons? Then I had a bright idea. I said that we boys would give some of our own coupons and collect the money for the dress between the eight of us. Taylor was delighted and said that he was satisfied and hoped that we'd be more sensible in the future. Even Haggar seemed pleased. He said that he was proud his boys had responded so well and he was sure Mr Taylor would carry a good opinion of the school for the rest of his life. During all this Elsie stood there looking glum, and as her face was still bright blue, Haggar suggested she went home. Then he asked the girls to leave the class. Only then did I realise that all was not well. Haggar solemnly told us, that although he was proud of his boys, he would still have to cane us! I can tell you Merv, it's really nice to get four of the best from a Headmaster who is really proud of you!! It's quite something. You ought to think yourself lucky that you're safely hidden away in Wales.

The funny thing was, that when Haggar met Shaw in the corridor later that day, he remarked on how surprised he was that Shaw wasn't involved in the plimsoll throwing incident. Shaw said that if he hadn't had to go to the doctors he probably would have been. So Haggar gave him four of the best for being insolent. When I was collecting the money and the coupons I asked Shaw for some, but he threatened to punch me on the nose. He gets upset very easily.

Dad wasn't very happy about the coupons but mum was furious. She said that if her coupons were going to be wasted on mere chits of girls, she'd soon have nothing to wear. Dad told me that now I was growing up, I should act in a more responsible manner, so I quickly reminded him of his story of blowing up a wall with a tube of toothpaste packed with gunpowder. He was my age at the time. At least we hadn't blown the girl to bits. He laughed and went off to Fire-watch. Lucinda has promised me she will never speak to Elsie again. When I pointed out that it wasn't her dress that got ruined she said she wouldn't speak to me either. I shall still publish her poem about the cat.

As we lost a term, we're only going to have a month's holiday this summer. I can't say that I mind that much. Of course, these days, life for you is one long holiday!

Cheerio,
Bill

27, Tudor Drive,
Llandudno Junction,
Caernarvonshire.
11th August 1941

Dear Bill,

I think your guess about the air-raids easing off was right. Eric wrote to say that at long last he's able to catch up on his sleep. I suppose that most of the Luftwaffe have been sent to Russia. Anyway, I'm glad that you're not still getting a pasting. Up here, there's nothing happening at all. In fact, it's beginning to get a bit boring. I've cut my reading down to three books a week because I've started to do some sketching and I've written quite a few poems. The dynamic tension is really working—an extra inch around the chest. During the week I get out and about as much as I can, which is fine, but not much fun on your own. In fact, I'm a bit scared that I shall start talking to myself—and you know what that means! Of course, as Vevlie says, it doesn't help with the four of us living in one room—especially when it's not your own. Still, there's a war on so one shouldn't complain.

Last Sunday the four of us went out into the country on a picnic and ended up by nearly getting lynched. We'd had a smashing day, Mum and Vev had dabbled their feet in a stream and Dad had tried to show me how to tickle trout—I got the idea but that was all. On the way home we came across this ruined cottage. No one had lived there for years and the garden was completely overgrown but there were these two apple trees laden down with ripe, red apples. Apart from the thermos, the two baskets were empty, so we got picking. As we got

159

near home we met up with all the holy-holy lot coming out of their chapels. By golly Bill, now I know what lepers feel like! You should have seen the looks we got. Picking apples on the Sabbath, you see. They even started pointing at us and muttering away in Welsh until Dad shouted at them, 'God help you if they drop a bomb on this place on a Sunday—because no one else will'. That shut them up. All the way home, Mum went on about him making a spectacle of himself, but Dad kept chuckling and saying, 'That told 'em, that told 'em'.

As you know, I've always liked Sundays, and that night I lay awake thinking about Sundays before the war. In fact, the very next day I sat down and wrote and essay called My Sundays. When we had no one coming, after we'd had our breakfast and a good argument, Dad would go out and cut or dig up what vegetables we needed, then work in the garden up until dinner time. Only gardening on Sundays. Shoe mending and things like that he would do on Saturday afternoons. After dinner, Dad would put on a clean shirt and Mum a good dress, then we'd all go for a walk. Eltham Park, Avery Hill and Blackheath. Sometimes we'd catch a 21 bus out to Farningham, go for a long walk, then have a pot of tea somewhere. Of course, Vev and Eric never came with us. She'd be off playing tennis and he'd be out on his motorbike, so it was just the three of us.

On the Sundays when we went over to see Uncle Bob and Auntie Cissie at Abbey Wood, there was a different routine. Mum would always take Cissie something from the garden or a pot of home made jam. While the women got on with the dinner, Dad, Bob and I would walk up to his allotment.

You've never met Bob. He's a big, round-faced Yorkshireman and is a road sweeper. On the way to the allotment, he'd tell us of all the things he'd found lying in the gutter that week. Money, earrings—he once found a gold tooth-pick! When we got to the allotment, we would all solemnly walk around it admiring the vegetables. Then it was back for dinner. I think it was meant as a joke but I'm still not quite sure, because Bob would often say, 'A fine bit of pork that, Cissie. Cost four shilling. Not much left for next week. Anyone want anymore?' No one had second helpings at Abbey Wood.

160

In the afternoon, I was given a book to read while they played whist in the front room. Bob always rolls his own cigarettes and so their house has this slightly scented smell. As soon as the clock struck five, Bob would say, 'Tea, Cissie' and he and Dad would then talk about politics while it was got ready. Afterwards, Cissie would give Mum some vegetables or a pot of jam, then we'd catch the tram home. When they came to us it was exactly the same—except instead of the allotment Dad would show Bob around the garden. The funny thing is, I can't remember being bored by all this. In fact, it was only when I came to write all this down, that I could see this pattern that kept on repeating itself. It made me wonder what would have happened, if just once Dad had said he didn't want to see Bob's allotment. I don't suppose we'd have been invited ever again.

Talking of patterns and habits, does your Mum do exactly the same thing on the same day week after week after week? Mine does. Monday it's out with the Belco tub for washing. First the bag of Blue Boy and the whites, then the coloured, finally, Dad's greasy overalls.

Mervyn's Mum and Dad all dressed up for a Sunday outing to Bob and Cissie

161

After she's mangled and hung everything out to dry, Mum scrubs the kitchen table. And on a Monday, it's always cold meat and bubble and squeak. Tuesday is ironing, mincemeat or rissoles. Wednesday, cleaning the bedrooms. Thursday, the front room and all the windows. Friday, whiten the front step, Cardinal red the back step, then shopping, and always fish for dinner. Do you suppose that mothers all over the country follow this same pattern? If you travelled from one end of Britain to the other, in an aeroplane on a Monday, I wonder if you would see the entire country festooned with washing? And on a Friday, millions of women on their hands and knees, busy whitening their front steps? If it's true, I hope no one tells Hitler. All he'd need to do, is invade Wales on a Sunday and he'd find the entire population in Chapel—apart from the four of us, that is.

Thinking about all this, I'm going to make darned sure I don't end up doing the same job day after day, for ever and ever. This is why I think that if I can be an actor, I'll never be bored. I suppose that if you wrote history books that would be different as well—unless you always wrote about Napoleon, which you seem to do at the moment. Try Oliver Cromwell for a change or Nelson.

Oh yes, Bob and Cissie. Mum told me something recently that you must promise to keep to yourself. She said it was because I was now old enough to be told such things. Bob and Cissie aren't my Uncle and Aunt at all! They're just friends of Mum and Dad. And they're not even married!!! How about that? Cissie's first husband was killed in the Great War and she gets a pension. If she and Bob actually got married she'd lose this pension—so they live together in sin! You'd never think it to look at them. That's all for now.

Your friend,

Merv

7, Nesbit Road,
Eltham, S.E.9.
31st August 1941

Dear Merv,

I'm afraid I've got very bad news. My grandmother was killed in an air raid a few days ago. Her house at Welling received a direct hit during the night from a 'hit and run' raider. The first I knew that anything was wrong, was when I heard shouting and crying very early one morning. It was only just dawn. I ran downstairs to find a policeman standing in the living room. Mum had collapsed with a slight heart attack and dad was sitting in a chair crying like a baby. I'd never seen him cry before so I knew it was something bad. When the policeman told me, I burst into tears too! I cuddled dad, the first time since I was a child. Then I put my arm around mum, but you have to be careful when she's having an attack because she can't get her breath.

Dad was the nearest next-of-kin, the policeman said. Aunt Edna, his eldest sister, is miles away in Camberwell. In any case, dad is the eldest son and his brother is away in the army. Dad had to go and identify the body. I wanted to go with him but they wouldn't let me. So I left mum with Mrs Collins and cycled over to Welling. I got there about 6.30. It was a gorgeous summer morning. The road was cordoned off but the Wardens let me through when I said who I was. The house was a complete wreck. Naturally I'm used to wreckage, but this one was different. It was a house I had known all my life. Walls, pictures, curtains, lamps, ornaments which I could remember since I was a baby, were all smashed or thrown about. It was difficult to work out where the rooms and passages had been because the roof had dropped on to part of the house. The Civil Defence men pointed to where they had found the body when I asked them. It seemed to be in the passage by the lavatory. Perhaps she had got up to go there when it happened?

The front room, where grandfather used to tell me his war stories, had one wall standing. I recognised it because it still had a photograph of him in army uniform hanging on it, with bits of wallpaper flapping across it in the breeze. The kitchen was a mess. Often on Sundays I

163

Bill's grandmother before the war

would cycle over to see granny. She would take me to the kitchen and give me some of her lovely bread-pudding, or let me dip bread in the fat that was cooking the roast. Nobody else's bread fat tasted like hers. The piano was lying on its side, hardly damaged. Grandfather never played it after he lost a finger working the machines in the Arsenal during the last war. He never let anybody touch it, and once he clipped my cousin Ron's ear for climbing on it when he was a baby.

The Wardens said she had died instantly. I think they were being kind. After all, how could they know for certain?

As I cycled home I still couldn't believe it had really happened. You never think these things are going to happen to you or your relatives. All through the Blitz I never thought that we, the family that is, were in any danger. Only other people get killed. I know it's daft, but that's how I felt. Now it had happened and I just couldn't stop crying every time I thought of it.

This crying business is a real problem. I never knew it was so hard to hold back tears until these last few days. When the news spread at school, I dreaded anybody mentioning it in case I burst into tears. Naturally, everybody was good about it but I felt so foolish. Haggar sent for me when he heard. He told me to sit down and said how sorry he was. I began to cry. He'd never seen me do that, not even when he caned me really hard. He asked me about my grandparents, and I told him one or two things. That set me blubbing again. Then he surprised me. He lit a cigarette. I never knew he smoked. I suppose he wouldn't do it in front of the pupils, especially as anyone caught smoking, even out of school, gets it in the neck.

Haggar said he knew what it was like to lose loved ones. He told me about his friends who had been killed fighting beside him in the last war. Eight, he said he'd lost. I thought of my own best friends, like you and Smithson, and it seemed an awful lot. He mentioned that his mother had died when he was away at the front. By the time he got leave she was buried; he never saw the coffin even. It seemed queer talking normally to Haggar. Usually you just answer questions, or think up an excuse to get out of trouble. Finally, he really surprised me. He said he knew how much I liked writing and advised me to write down how I felt. Don't show it to anybody, just write it for yourself, he said. For a mathematician, I thought that was quite clever. It would help me relieve my feelings. Whether Miss Wilcox has told him I keep a diary I don't know. He told me he still had letters he had written in the trenches; letters so personal he had never shown them to his wife. They were his sad secrets, he told me. They had stopped him from going mad.

I keep seeing granny's face. I want to remember it always. The body is being kept at the undertakers as it is so hot. Dad said it was something he would never want mum or me to see. I never realised how much he loved her. He never cried at all at my grandfather's funeral. I never want to see that street in Welling again. We had such happy times there, especially at Christmas. I hate the bloody Germans more than ever now. I hope that thousands and thousands of them die in Russia. Can't write anymore. We are all getting ready for the funeral tomorrow which will be awful.

Cheerio,

Bill

P.S. We were playing cricket when Roberts slashed a ball really hard. Haggar was passing and caught it one handed. He must have been a good cricketer when he was young.

27, Tudor Drive,

Llandudno Junction,

Caernarvonshire.

4th September 1941

Dear Bill,

You poor old chap. I feel so sorry for you and I wish there was something I could say to help but I'm afraid I don't know the right words. Anyway, I don't suppose there are any right words at a time like this. Still, Haggar seems to have been very understanding. He sounds like a decent bloke underneath all that caning. I only met your grandmother once. We'd been out cycling somewhere and you decided to call in on her. She'd just baked some rock cakes and gave us one each with butter on them. I'll always remember how good they tasted. She was a lovely lady.

I told Dad what had happened. As you know, he and Mum were into Spiritualism for a while after Stella died. Dad reckons that it's only the body that dies. The spirit lives on. They are still there, only we can't see or talk to them anymore. It's the same as hearing someone on a gramophone record. The voice is printed into the record the same as the spirit is printed into time. I couldn't quite follow that.

I'm coming home. We all are. I'm not quite sure when it will be, but very soon. Here's how it happened. We had a letter from Eric. He asked to be released from war work in the Arsenal and they agreed. He's going into the army.

I don't think that this event will alter the course of the war all that much, but it's certainly altered things for the rest of the family. The Lloyds had started making life pretty unpleasant in all sorts of small ways and it was beginning to get us all down. Big arguments over one potato—I ask you, how petty minded can you get? Mum had already started to look for some new digs when the letter arrived. Of course, Eric going into the army meant that Kenward Road would be empty and that really worried Dad. He thought about it for a day, then made up his mind. 'Bugger the job and bugger North Wales, we're going home!'

Mum was so pleased she kissed him on the cheek. And that's something I've never seen her do before.

So, after all this time you're going to have to put up with me again. I hope there's enough room for the two of us at Eltham Hill. I suppose I'll end up in your class. This Lucinda you keep writing about sounds just my type. I like girls with long hair.

Will write again as soon as I know the date we're coming back. I'm sure all this has been a great shock to you, so will leave it at that.

Your friend,

Merv

Eric in the army

7, Nesbit Road,
Eltham, S.E.9.
7th September 1941

Dear Merv,

I said granny's funeral would be awful and it was. They brought the body back from the undertakers to my Aunt Ada's house in Abbey Wood. Her house is nearest the cemetery. Dad and Mum went by tram, but I walked across Plumstead Common and down the King's Highway. Really I wanted to be alone. It was a very hot day and the sun beat down on my head. I wore sunglasses for the first time. I've been getting headaches lately, probably from reading and writing a lot during the rotten blackout last winter. I wondered whether they might be caused by firebomb glare, but Dr. Evans says no.

Although I had the day off from school I felt very sad. Grandad died in a heatwave, now granny was being buried during one. I shall always think of death when the sun shines. Not a pleasant prospect! Aunt Ada also had the body because she's the only one in the family with a big front-room. The coffin was set on tressles, almost covered with flowers. The black-edged cards had the usual doggerel chosen by my relatives to express their grief. Not exactly Shakespeare but their hearts are in the right place. I bought my own bunch of flowers and put on the card a quotation from 'Peter Pan'. Do you remember we saw Charles Laughton in it at the Lyceum before the war? Peter says, 'To die would be an awfully big adventure.' Dad had quoted from Gilbert:

> 'Is life a boon?
> If so, it must befall,
> That Death, whene'er he call,
> Must call too soon.'

Of course, he loves Gilbert and Sullivan. This was from 'The Yeomen of the Guard'. It was a better choice than mine, considering how granny died.

At 3.15pm, the hearse and cars, four of them, arrived. It was appallingly hot in the car. I thought we would suffocate, even though

169

appaling for, in spite of the open windows, the hot air almost asphixiated you. As we rode up the steep hill in the cemetery to the chapel I swiftly read the inscriptions on some of the tombs. Snatches of "Gone but not forgotten", "At Rest", "Jesus took him for a sunbeam" crowded upon me, things written by simple people, bewildered by their grief and lack of understanding as to why they had to grieve. In the chapel the usual toneless gabbly was presented to us and the ceremony at the grave was little better. I could not but think, as I gazed down at Granny's coffin in the grave that Grandfather's shell was just below it. As a matter of fact the whole afternoon was full of

Diary entry for Bill's grandmother's funeral

we had the windows down. I couldn't help thinking that I've only been in a car three times—and two of those have been to funerals. The other time was when a friend of dad's took us to Brooklands Race Track before the war. As we rose slowly up the steep hill in the cemetery, I read the inscriptions on the tombstones—'Gone but not forgotten', 'At rest', and worst still, on a youngster's grave, 'Jesus took him for a sunbeam'. There was the usual tuneless babble from the vicar in the chapel, and then we were out in the oven-like heat, round the open grave where we buried grandfather last year.

As I gazed into that terrible hole I thought of grandfather's rotting shell, only a few feet beneath. It was only afterwards, as we walked back to the cars, that dad told me his mother's mother was also buried in that grave. So his granny was down there too! I was surprised. He hadn't said anything before. She died in 1921. There is a faded photograph of her on the wall at Aunt Edna's; one of those where the face appears out of a sort of hazy circle. She looked lovely but the picture frightened me as a child. I think this was because there was also a photograph of her coffin beside it. Yes, there really was. They were on a landing. And as there were three flights of stairs with really dark landings, they used to seem very spooky, so I'd always run by them without looking.

Dad was in tears most of the time. All the family cried much more for granny than they did for grandfather. Aunt Edna actually collapsed when we got back to the house. She fell against the gate and everybody began to shout for my Uncle Jim (her husband), who was way behind in another car as he was only an 'in-law'. I think she fainted partly from the heat as well as grief. In the evening the men, including me, went for a drink at a pub, but there was no booze-up like there had been after grandfather's funeral. It would have been wrong considering the way granny died.

I overheard some of my aunts talking about my great- grandmother's death in 1921. Dad was away fighting the Arabs in Mesopotamia at the time, and he loved her so much that he seems to have gone sort of mad. They said that a lot of the trouble dad got into then was because of this. I've heard all his other military prison stories—of how they put leg-irons on him when he was in Poona—but he never told me that he'd deserted and gone on the run all over the desert. Still, I can understand how he loved her. I also loved my granny and the way she died makes me very angry.

I walked back up Shooters Hill and on to Eaglesfield. It was a lovely evening with a wonderful view of Woolwich, the whole loop of the Thames, and the big ships in the docks. I expect you know the view, but of course now, we've got barrage balloons. I can't remember what a clear sky was like without them; they only bring them down when it's cloudy. I felt on top of the world, almost level with the balloons. Perhaps I was level, because it's really high on top of Shooters Hill. Did you ever get taken up there on a New Years' Eve before the war, to see all the ships lit up, and hear them sound off their hooters dead on midnight? Dad took me once, probably because he'd been on the 'Orsova' and loves anything to do with ships and the sea.

It was gorgeous to feel the breeze at last as the sun went down, but it was a very sad day which I shall never forget. And I shall never go to church again. I only did it for granny's sake.

I'm really glad you're coming back at last. As you can guess, I'm feeling pretty down in the dumps. Besides, we're doing selections from 'Hamlet' for the Christmas concert so you'll come in handy—to play Laertes to my Hamlet!! I haven't told any of the girls the news. It's best not to give them too much of a shock all at once. Which reminds me. You're welcome to any of them except Lucinda. She's mine, so keep your muddy paws off her!

Talk about a country cousin. Have you got a Welsh accent? Let me know what time you'll be arriving at Well Hall station and I'll try to be there. Will it seem funny to come back to the same station you left almost exactly two years ago? Of course, you don't know yet, but I'll bet it will!! Two years. And what a two years it's been!

Cheerio,
Bill

172

27, Tudor Drive,
Llandudno Junction,
Caernarvonshire.
9th September 1941

Dear Bill,

Your letter arrived this morning. Glad to hear that your grandmother's funeral went well and that now it's all over and done with. It sounds as though you gave her a good send off, although I expect you'll still feel sad for a bit.

I'll keep this short as I want to catch the post. We shall be arriving home this Saturday, the 12th. I'm afraid I can't tell you the time, but it will probably be quite late. I like the idea of you waiting for us at Well Hall station—because we'll be getting off at Lewisham! Dad has worked out that with all our cases, it will be easier for us to pick up a bus or tram at Lewisham and get off at the Yorkshire Grey—or what's left of it. A much shorter walk home. Yes, I expect it will seem very strange to be back home after all this time. Two years and ten days exactly. If you're not doing anything, you could come round on Sunday afternoon.

Your friend,
Merv

P.S.   Why don't we let Lucinda decide for herself?